A WARNING ABOUT YOUR FUTURE ENSLAVEMENT THAT
YOU WILL DISMISS AS A COLLECTION OF SHORT
FICTION AND ESSAYS BY KIT POWER
First Published in 2017

Cover design by Kit Power

This one is for all my beta readers – past, present and future. Thanks for your sage council, and apologies for all the times I didn't listen.

Contents

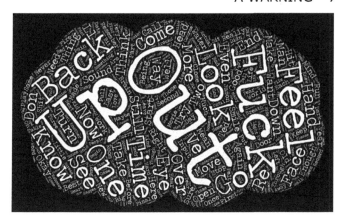

HIGHEST CLEARANCE/ULTRAVIOLET BAND EYES ONLY/

CASE REPORT FILE 7776293824/10/15

THE ATTACHED DOCUMENT REPRESENTS COLLECTED BRAIN DUMPS CREATED BY FORMER CITIZEN AND MINISTRY OF INFORMATION ORANGE BAND CLEARANCE, DESIGNATION K-POX. CASE STUDY RETAINED FOR HIGHEST CLEARANCE AS AN OBJECT LESSON IN THE NEED FOR THE MINISTRY TO REMAIN VIGILANT AND CONSISTENT WHEN ENFORCING LIMITATIONS ON THE RE-RELEASE OF INFORMATION BACK INTO THE POPULATION, AS WELL AS SOME OUTSTANDING SECURITY QUESTIONS (SEE REPORT CONCLUSION). THIS ALSO REINFORCES THE WISDOM OF CURRENT POLICY REGARDING THE PROHIBITION ON ALL MATTERS FICTIONAL, AND MANY MATTERS HISTORICAL. OUR FAILURE TO ENFORCE THIS PROHIBITION IN A TIMELY FASHION LED K-POX TO PAY THE ULTIMATE PRICE.

NEVER FORGET.

If I get caught with this, they're going to fucking kill me.

The wiring is pretty ridiculous, but I think I can figure it out.

What was it doing there in the first place? It was supposed to be a standard storage unit; most of those rooms are just full of olden hard drives, data sticks, those shiny disk things...

Aha! We have power.

...And there it sat, under a plastic dust cover. Fabulously complicated. Clearly *not* data storage. Obviously analytic in design. Old – you can tell just by the interface, the tubes – but so elaborate...

Boot-up is taking ages. At least it's quiet. Quick glance up the basement steps. Force of habit. No one coming.

I kept it hidden as best I could, piling dead drives in front of it. Inspecting it whenever duties took me back to the storage unit. Took measurements, too. No way to tell the exact age, of course. Pre-war. We couldn't make anything this complex now. Lost the knack...

Okay, it's finished initializing.

I press the big red button, and the glass sample tube slides out of the side of the machine. I pick up the toenail I kept from last night.

There's probably something stupid about using my own DNA as a sample. Of course, when you pile up the stupidity of hiding the machine instead of immediately alerting my superiors, then stealing the machine and hiding it in my basement, *then* manually rewiring the output device to hopefully transmit legible information to a brain dump feed without frying my mind in the process – I mean, basically, my only hope is that the fuck-ups cancel each other out, somehow...

Still, I hesitate for a second, wondering what the outputs will *be* exactly; what secret information this machine can extract.

What I will learn.

Fuck it, only one way to find out. I release the toenail, and the glass tube swallows it with an almost slurping noise, sucking the sample into the guts of the machine.

The tube retracts. Lights on the side flash. There's a grinding noise, followed by a clicking. The clicking goes for some time, then stops.

Then starts again.

More lights flash.

Then they stop.

Nothing happens.

I guess maybe it doesn't—

10 – A WARNING

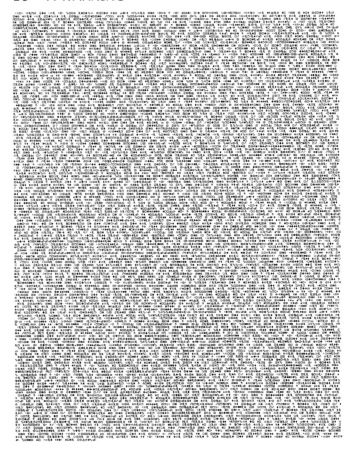

...Heave vomit hot bile oh fu—
<INPUT ENDS>

<INPUT BEGINS>

Next day. Okay, let's try this again. Turns out there was an incompatibility between the output code and the brain dump software at my end. Pretty sure I've fixed that now. Bloody hope so. Don't want to go through that again.

Meanwhile in the Bad News Department, turns out it *was* dumb to use my own sample first. The machine will only output once per individual DNA sample. I tried re-running my own sample again and the output was identical, even with the fixes I've made at this end. That might be down to anti-information replication protocols in the brain dump writer software, now I think about it. Yet another irritating side effect of our inability to make new copies of data sources. Whatever. Way out of my pay-grade, that stuff. Still, the mangled output is infuriating. If only we still had decryption software...

I take out a plastic packet containing a single human hair. I think about how I'd seen the dead hair stuck to the back of the woman's coat in the elevator, how I'd snatched it without thinking, not even considering what I'd do or say if I'd been mistaken and it had still been attached. Stupid. Going to need to get smarter about sample collection.

Well, that's tomorrow's problem. The tube accepts the hair eagerly. I grip the side of the desk this time, teeth gritted, watching the flashing lights. Waiting for them to—

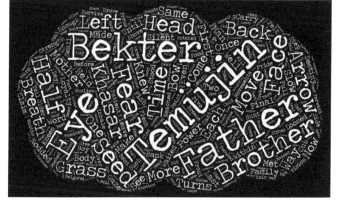

Temüjin lay in the tall grass, stolid and unmoving. His breath was slow and shallow, and he was sure that any displacement in the grass was disguised by the warm breeze. His eyes tracked his half-seed brother as he made his way down the bank towards the stream, fishing pole in hand. Bekter was five years older than Temüjin and had the lean and hardened body of a hunter but, even with the extra strength he carried from all the food he'd stolen from the mouths of Temüjin's full-seed brothers and sister, he stood only a half head taller than Temüjin himself. Temüjin was confident he would be able to beat the half-seed in a test of strength. Should it come to that.

Temüjin's eyes followed Bekter's movements as the older boy found a spot by the bank, sun to his face so he cast no shadow on the water, and turned stone as their father had taught them. Temüjin observed this process, blinking only rarely, waiting until his half-brother's back was barely moving with breath. He knew now that all Bekter's focus would be on the stream, all senses bent to the slightest ripple on the surface of the water.

Unmindful of his own exposed back.

Temüjin turned to his left and met the gaze of Khasar. His full-seed brother met his eyes levelly and without fear. *Good.* Temüjin reached to his left, silently grasping his notched bow and moving it in front of him. The tiny whickering noise of the grass to his right informed him that Khasar was mirroring his move.

They had discussed this many times, first in general terms and then, as Bekter and Belgutei's theft became more brazen, with more serious planning. Temüjin had raised the matter with Mother, remonstrating with her to discipline the half-seeds, make them see their responsibility to the whole family, not just their own interests. But Mother had refused, telling Temüjin that they needed every hunter to stay strong. That the family unit was already too small to endure the loss of any member. That only together could the eight of them survive until Temüjin was old enough, powerful enough, to reclaim his father's role within the greater tribe.

'You must be patient, Bear Cub,' she told him. 'Now we are small; every part needs every other part to survive. We must not be weakened. The bonds of loyalty are all that keep us from the End Sleep.'

Temüjin nodded in assent, but within his own council, he had formulated a different proposition. Loyalty was forged through fear. Fear alone. The half-seeds did not fear hunger because they kept the fat of the kill for themselves. Their loyalty was only to their mother and dead father, not to Temüjin and *his* siblings, *his* flesh. They knew who Temüjin was, who he would someday grow to be. Hadn't Mother told them all? The stories of his destiny on the endless cold nights when hunger gnawed the bones and the icy snow grasped at the doors of the tents, threatening to steal the life breath from their bodies?

They knew.

But they did not fear.

There was only one way to make them fear him, one way to ensure the survival of his true kin. In this way, Mother was weak, he knew. They were her flesh too. She drove Temüjin to his destiny, but was blind to the implications for them – ever subservient to their half-seed younger brother, with his powerful build and flaming hair and cold, calculating gaze.

Their pride was offended so they held the power of their seniority over Temüjin and his siblings, took food from their mouths, and claimed his kills as their own. It was this last that finally sealed their fate – when they took the larch and fish that Khasar and Temüjin had caught. That evening, as they made their toilet some distance from their camp, the two brothers laid their strategy.

And now it was time. Temüjin lifted himself up with

his arms, bringing his knees forward, then sat back on his haunches, head still concealed within the grass. Khasar did the same, and once more they faced each other. Temüjin saw his own resolve and clarity of purpose reflected in his brother's eyes, and it pleased him. He nodded, once, and with no other word, no further communication, they rose to standing height, bows held in front of them, notched arrows pointing at the dirt.

Bekter had held his position, poised and utterly focused forward. They knew from experience that he would register little from behind him while so bent to his task, but, at the same time, they knew all too well the folly and danger inherent in underestimating the instincts of the hunted.

They moved in concert to the edge of the grass, creeping with the same well-practiced stealth they employed when stalking rodents, until they stood clear of the grass line. Here, the soil was sandy and dry, which made moving silently relatively easy, providing one was patient.

They were, and, with achingly slow progress, they circled outwards, covering Bekter's back with their eyes, only glancing at the ground to place the next step. Temüjin remembered playing Boulders with his brothers and sister, moving in silence towards his blindfolded father, and the overwhelming pride he felt the first time he grabbed his father's staff without being *pointed*.

He felt that same pride now, as he stalked Bekter, that same surety of purpose, of destiny. He was about his father's work and, when the warm breeze caressed his face, he felt his father's blessing carried on it, urging him forward in his task, approving. The cool sand sifted between his toes, whispering unintelligible words on the edge of his hearing. He tracked Khasar's movements with his peripheral vision, twin jaws slowly closing on their stationary prey. When they had reached a distance of five paces, Temüjin halted. His eyes remained focused on the back of the half-seed's neck and with his peripheral vision he registered that Khasar had also stopped.

Waiting.

They stood in that configuration for several breaths, the two boys with their bows and the young man with his spear, each focused with total concentration on the target in front of them, on the moment of the hunt just before the strike, where time stretches thin and long and each breath seems to contain an eternity of weight, of thought.

Temüjin inhaled.

He remembers the face of his father, the last time, the day Temüjin was left with Dai Setsen. His father explains the meaning of his young son's betrothal, how it will unite the two clans, once he reaches the age of manhood and takes Börte as his bride. Such a strong man, his father, such a powerful man. Such a wise man.

He exhaled, seeing his mounted father departing across the plain, hair hanging at his back in a loosely tangled knot. The horse will carry him to the Tartars, and, recognising him and fearing him, they will poison him under the banner of hospitality, and Temüjin will learn of this and leave his new clan to be at his dying father's side, but a slow horse and the quick poison will prevent him from ever again hearing his father's voice. For the hundredth time, the thousandth, he vows that his vengeance on the Tartars will be swift, brutal, total.

Inhale.

His mother stands by his side as he claims his father's mantle as leader, but the others laugh at this upstart cub-who-would-be-king, and they cast Temüjin and his family out, declare them ghosts, and leave them to starve on the indifferent plains. He and his family leave the tribe, heads held high, defiant, and Temüjin makes another vow – that when he comes of age, he will return to claim his destiny.

Exhale.

Mother schools him – by day in the arts of hunting and combat and war, at night in the tales of his ancestors and in the reality of politics. He learns about what makes a truly great leader: cunning, strength, power and the willingness to use it; the nature and necessity of alliances and loyalties, the prices and dangers and prizes of treachery; but above all, the strength of purpose that can only come when all who know your name fear your wrath above all.

He learns his lessons well.

He inhaled once more and, as he did so, he nocked his arrow and raised the stock, fingers loosely holding the draw string. Again, the corner of his eye reported that Khasar was mirroring his actions.

Temüjin nodded, once. Then he spat. The saliva carried far enough to land near Bekter's feet, creating a small patch of damp sand.

Bekter stiffened at the sound, finally aware that he had been outflanked, aware too of what the gesture signified. Temüjin waited patiently, impassively, for his half-brother to assess the situation and draw his conclusions.

After a couple of breaths, the first shallow, the second ragged but deeper, Bekter turned to face his fate. He turned away from Temüjin, so the first face he saw was that of Khasar. Bekter looked concerned, even scared, until his head turned fully, and his eyes meet Temüjin's. Fear give way to recognition, then to terror, and resignation. It happened fast, but Temüjin noted every step, every phase. He filed them away for later consideration.

They faced each other, silent, breathing, calm. Temüjin could see that Bekter meant to speak and he decided to allow him that much. He had chosen to face his death with honour; he was to be permitted a last word.

'The lark and the fish were mine. Do not punish Belgutei for my wrongs. Allow him to serve you and yours faithfully, as I should have.'

It is well spoken, thought Temüjin.

'You have my word. If he turns from the path of disloyalty and greed, he shall not fear my bow or blade.'

Bekter inclined his head, in supplication, respect, thanks. As he straightened, Temüjin loosed his arrow. It pierced the skin above Bekter's left collarbone, propelled with enough force that the point protruded from his shoulder. Khasar's first shot was lower and punctured Bekter's chest, near the bottom of his ribcage. The sharp arrow head drove into his lung, causing it to collapse, and Bekter's knees started to give. Before he fell, Temüjin and Khasar had shot twice more each, nocking and loosing their arrows in practiced, fluid movements. Each arrow struck flesh, puncturing his stomach, his chest, his neck.

He sank to his knees, arms limp at each side, palms facing out. Temüjin walked over to him slowly, his final arrow nocked. He stepped into Bekter's field of vision, watched the pupils moving as the eyes struggled to focus. Finally, Bekter's gaze grew sharp and met Temüjin's eyes.

Temüjin nodded one final time, before bringing the bow up and shooting the last arrow into his brother's left eye. Bekter's spirit left in a rush, flying into the End Sleep, and his body collapsed, his life's blood soaking into the sandy soil of the Steppe.

Temüjin and Khasar left their brother's body where it fell and headed back to the family camp to tell Mother. She would be angry, Temüjin reflected, but she would understand. In time.

Loyalty comes first. All else is dust.

...What the actual *fuck?*

<INPUT ENDS>

<INPUT BEGINS>

Can't sleep. Too excited. Too many questions. I've re-run the brain dump recording output over and over again. I have it memorised. The events. The vivid scene. The names. Most of all, the names.

I've run them through the pre-war histories we've recovered so far, and there's nothing there. But of course, that's only the history that's in the public domain. There's terabytes of undifferentiated historical data still requiring vetting and approval, all sitting on the Ministry mainframe.

Maybe these names are on there. Maybe...

Fuck it - I need to unplug, try to think.

<INPUT ENDS>

<INPUT BEGINS>

Next day.

It's real.

I found him today, on the mainframe. Temüjin. He's real; he *happened.* It's all in one of the unverified history files – he grew up to be called Genghis Khan, and apparently ruled half the planet before he died – all listed officially as 'unproven,' of course.

Except I've fucking proven it.

The machine works.

I knew its function was to read junk DNA from the samples - the user interface makes that much clear, if little else. And I knew it would produce some kind of interpretable data output, which is why I rigged up a way to plug my brain-jack into the machine. Hoping the outputs would be close enough to my own user generated dumps to be understandable. And what these outputs and my research have now proven is that junk DNA is *not* junk. Somehow, it has encoded within it historical data. Data the machine can read; data I've been able to convert into brain dump output. Allowing me to relive history.

Holy *fuck*.

<INPUT ENDS>

<INPUT BEGINS>

Okay. Calmer now. Not actually calm, mind, but...okay. Okay. I've got one point of data. That's not a line. A human hair output data about a historical figure that once ruled the world. Probably did. So I may have discovered a machine that could single-handedly transform the work of the Ministry and save decades of work.

Of course, I did that by stealing it and then basically fucking about with it until it worked. So there's that.

Point is, I need to figure out more about this machine and the outputs, so I'm going to try this bird feather. The output should be primitive. Maybe unintelligible. I'm ready for that.

I need to test my hypothesis.

I have to know this thing works.

Here we g—

The four chickens were adopted young, within a couple of weeks of coming of age – measured by chickens, naturally enough, from the time they start laying eggs. They were taken from their siblings – two brown, two white – and placed in a small domestic garden. The home they were given was spacious, with a nesting box and feeding area. For three days they were kept in there, fussing and fidgeting and engaging in displays of dominance.

Sorting out the pecking order.

In this period, they met their first God.

The first God was a hen-human. She brought them food, water, changed the bedding straw, took the eggs, and gave them foraging seed in the afternoon. They named her C'ra, which is chicken for 'Mother'. They loved her (as much as chickens can love, which is not, sad to say, a great deal) and revered her, and attempted to reward her by laying regularly.

C'ra often set them loose in the garden of an afternoon. There they ate the grass, dug for worms and grubs, and shat on the patio.

Here, they met for the first time their second God.

He was a cock-human. He also gave them foraging seed, and sometimes he would crumb bread and throw it for them. He scraped out and cleaned their home every two weeks, removing all the accumulated shit and matted straw, and replacing it with clean. Though they saw him less frequently, his kindness meant they revered him too. They called him R'ak, which is chicken for 'Father'. In deference to him, they tried their best to shit in a particular section of the dwelling, to make his work easier. (Sadly, chickens are largely incontinent, and this effort was therefore not hugely successful.)

Three weeks after their arrival, the four chickens were loose in the garden, enjoying a late summer afternoon bug hunt. C'ra and R'ak were sat in chairs, talking in the gabbling human noise, holding their strange featherless wings together, and drinking a fluid from brown bottles, which smelt to the chickens like rancid water. After an exchange, R'ak got up and walked into the Human House.

He returned with a miniature human on his wing.

The chick-human smelled like a cock-human to the chickens, but it was so small they couldn't be sure. When standing, it only just came up to R'ak's thigh, and was pink-fleshed save for shoes and comically large white pants. The chick-human made oddly pitched gurgling noises that made the chickens' heads hurt, but R'ak and C'ra smiled and cooed at every sound, apparently immune to the pain.

While the chickens marvelled at this, R'ak let the chick-human go, pointing in the general direction of the garden.

What followed was pandemonium.

The chick-human uttered a shriek that pierced the chickens' skulls like a drill, and then charged. Its gait was lumbering and ungainly, but its purpose was unmistakable. The chickens turned as one to the source of the noise, and beheld what dwelt in its eyes.

What they saw filled them with dread; they knew one of their own.

They scattered at its approach, understanding instinctively that the herd was a bigger target. This elicited another awful shriek from the creature, and it put on an alarming burst of speed. The pink chick-human pursued one, then another, changing course seemingly at random. The chickens clucked and squawked their terror to R'ak and C'ra, but their lamentations fell on deaf ears – the two Gods simply observed, smiling.

Quickly, the chickens realised that the creature would pursue whoever it was closest to, and so began a quite horrible game of Tag, where each hunted animal would run close enough to another to draw the staggering monster's attention, until all the chickens were ragged and terrified.

Finally, one of them, more through luck than judgment, fled back into their new home. There was a moment of pure existential horror as the creature began pursuit, but C'ra suddenly intervened, plucking up the awful noise-producing thing with a tone that implied admonishment.

The other chickens, relieved at the notion that they had sanctuary, retreated in short order to their home, and cowered until the creature was removed from the garden.

They had met their third God. They named it B'rok, which is chicken for 'Chaos'.

B'rok became a constant source of terror over the following weeks. It would kick the side of their home, and bang on the wire roof of their run. It would sometimes feed them bread but it would break it too big, causing the chickens to fight, and often it would only wave the bread at them before simply consuming it, producing its hateful sound the whole time.

The afternoon garden forages became fraught also – the chickens simply could not relax, always on edge, awaiting the arrival of the pink bundle of miniature malevolence and the inevitable chase that would ensue.

The chickens grew increasingly agitated and, despite their continued and sustained prayers, their Gods offered neither relief nor succour.

The final straw came during one such chase session. B'rok had become more and more agile, faster, and harder to avoid. A couple of times it had managed to grab at the tails of the slower brown hens, and the shrieks from B'rok that followed such moments were excruciating.

On this particular occasion, B'rok had managed to corner one of the white hens – the head hen, as it happened. R'ak and C'ra were indifferent, sitting and making noises. The head hen was frozen in panic. B'rok laid both hands on her wings and squeezed, gurgling its demonic noise directly into her face, vibrating her thin skull and utterly enraging her tiny chicken brain.

She was the head hen, and she'd got there the way head hens always do. The paralysis broke all at once, and she did what came naturally.

She pecked.

Her beak pierced the fleshy lump in the centre of B'rok's face. She tasted hot flesh and blood. B'rok jumped back, stumbled and fell, then threw his head back and bellowed.

The head hen thought the sound was wonderful, like music.

So fascinated was she by the beautiful noise (and also by the feel of fresh blood and meat in her belly), she was scarcely aware of the two other Gods running over to investigate.

C'ra swept the suddenly-musical thing up into her arms, breaking the head hen's spell, and, too late, she became aware of R'ak swinging his foot towards her.

The blow lifted her off her feet. She collided with the wooden fence and landed badly, winded. Even in her shock she saw R'ak closing in again, making a noise she'd never heard before, deep and loud. She understood he had turned Predator, and meant to kill her. Instinct took over. She fled into her home.

She remained in there for several minutes, until the fear faded. She ventured out of the hutch and into the enclosed run, but all the Gods had gone, and the other chickens were back inside with her.

The chickens went about their business, and then the Gods returned. C'ra was cradling B'rok, who was still making that sweet sound. The injury to his face was covered, but the head hen could still smell the blood.

R'ak opened the cage, and the chickens shrank back, fearing another attack. Instead, he grabbed their water and removed it from the cage. He pointed at B'rok, making that same low, loud noise, then at the head hen, then at their water. Then, with slow deliberation, he poured it all out over the grass, before throwing the empty container back in the hutch. He then went to the Food Place, removed The Lid, and took out a cup of foraging seed – their afternoon food. He pointed again at B'rok's injury, then at the head hen, then he scattered the seeds on the ground outside the cage.

The cup and lid were replaced, and the Gods left.

The chickens were distraught – it was warm, they had been chased, they were thirsty – but the Gods were indifferent to their lamentations. They became hungry too, and could see the seeds on the ground, but their beaks were not long enough to reach them. Instead, they had to watch as local birds, drawn by the commotion, feasted on their seeds before flying off, unafraid. Their territory had been violated.

The chickens became angry.

That night, after a full afternoon and evening of no food and no water, they held conference in the sleeping area. Through clucks, movement, and scratching, they expressed dismay, despair, hunger, fear, anger. Their Gods had forsaken them. They had given the chickens over to B'rok, and punished them when their leader stood up to him.

B'rok had turned the other Gods against them.

The head hen waited for a moment, then scratched once with her left foot, decisively. The others fell silent at once.

Our Gods have forsaken us. B'rok is to blame. B'rok rules them.

B'rok is our enemy. B'rok makes the Bad Noise that pains us so. B'rok chases, hurts. B'rok grows bigger, stronger, faster.

The head hen let this sink in, feeling the fear and rage rising in her sisters. Letting it build. Then:

B'rok tastes of prey.

The others burst in excited song, happy, anxious.

Hungry.

B'rok tastes of prey, the head hen repeated. *B'rok is our Predator, but B'rok tastes like prey.*

B'rok is dangerous. B'rok is small.

Sisters. Let us use our Magic.

Sisters, let us cast the ritual.

For the next week, things went on as before. C'ra and R'ak returned to their roles, providing food and water. And of an afternoon, B'rok terrorised the chickens and chased them around their former garden paradise. They knew better than to fight back, and instead fled to their home, only emerging again when C'ra or R'ak took B'rok away.

Over the week, each laid one egg in the Perch rather than the Nest. These eggs were hidden in a small pile of straw. The Gods did not disturb the Perch apart from during the Cleans, and this was not due to happen for several days yet. The chickens were restless during this period; uneasy. They possessed only limited awareness, but some part of their animal brains understood that what they were about to do was dangerous.

Forbidden.

Still, on the night of the perfect half-moon, under the light of judgment, the chickens placed their eggs on the floor of the Perch. They stood, beaks facing in, and waited for the ritual to take them.

They all moved as one, jabbing forwards and opening the eggs. The yellow and clear fluids poured together in a sticky mass, mingling with the shit and straw and creating a paste.

Again as one, each pecked, piercing the yolks, freeing the yellow fluid to mix and swirl. The head hen moved into the centre and the others formed a triangle, with her as the eye. She scratched and scratched, her feet smearing the fluid, drawing crude shapes and sigils in the paste with her claws. The others just stared, unmoving.

Several minutes passed before the symbols were complete, then the head hen raised her beak. She clucked once. Immediately, the other hens jabbed, opening three wounds in her wings. She flapped, small droplets of blood splashing the walls, until eventually a few drops fell from her wing feathers into the circle she had drawn.

As this happened, she began her song. The other chickens joined in, their voices mixing in disharmony. The sound was chickens, yet unlike any sound a chicken had been heard to make by humans. It was eerie and discordant. It rose in the air, aided by the moon-rays, and wafted in through the brick wall of the house, into the ears of the sleeping Gods.

⚠

Time inside the ritual had no meaning. The chickens could feel their power rising, feel it mingling, becoming greater than the sum of its parts. They felt the Magic rise from them. Felt it touch the mind of a sleeper, then wrap around it like a snake. Felt the slumbering God rise.

The head hen gave her orders, careful not to break the chant. To hold two thoughts in her mind at once was an act of almost impossible difficulty, but hatred was ever a strong motivator. And she did hate, so very much.

Eventually, they heard the door to the house open, and they stopped their song. The Magic had taken root; the ritual had served its purpose.

They left the Perch in a flurry of feathers and a scrabble of claws, tumbling down the run in their haste. There, they saw R'ak. His head was glowing faintly with the residue from the Magic. His face was relaxed, eyes open but unseeing. He closed the thick-glassed door behind him, gently.

In his arms, he held the sleeping B'rok.

The night air was cold, and it began to stir as R'ak walked over to the door of the hutch. As he reached out to open up, the arm supporting B'rok's head fell away, and the chick-human awoke with a start. Immediately, it began to make that sweet noise again, the musical sound that had so pleased the head hen. As the bolt on the hutch was drawn, and the door swung open, she understood in a flash of recognition why the sound was so pleasing to her senses.

It was the sound of cornered prey.

R'ak placed B'rok down indifferently on the floor of the run, plucking one of those small featherless wings off his own as it tried to grasp him. R'ak locked the door and stepped back. The moon lit his face. He was smiling.

B'rok made the sweet noise louder than ever, and began trying to stand. The ground was slippery with shit and spilled water, and 'B'rok was still groggy from sleep.

The chickens' minds responded to the imperative in the sound, and they swiftly surrounded B'rok before it could rise.

They pecked. It howled. They pecked some more. It howled again and flailed about, but it was too uncoordinated. Too disoriented.

Too weak.

Their attacks became more insistent, more confident, as each got the taste. The blood and flesh and the sweet, sweet song of the prey filled them up and drove them on. Blood mingled with the shit and straw and water. It looked black in the moonlight. R'ak looked without seeing, and smiled on.

Eventually, long after they'd feasted on those delicious, delicate eyes; once the thrashing had become feeble and ceased altogether, the wonderful noise ceased. But by then the blood frenzy was upon them, and they pecked and pecked and pecked and pecked and pecked.

...Don't vomit. Don't Vomit. Don't

<INPUT ENDS>

<INPUT BEGINS>

Okay, so I managed to look up 'chickens' at work. Turns out they became extinct sometime around The War – a lot of domesticated and farm breeds bought it during the conflict, to judge from what I saw today in the unauthorised history files. Which in this particular case was probably just as well, to be honest.

Just how fucking stupid were we?

Anyway. I've made some adjustments to the settings on the machine. There's an odd distancing to the outputs, like the events I'm seeing are being...reported somehow. I'm assuming it's a feature of the underpinning software,

\<Of course you're assuming that. You're an idiot.\>

...but there's a bunch of settings that relate to this function which, to be honest, I don't fully understand, so who knows? Still, it's worth trying to fix it. Hopefully the changes I've made should remove the effect, get me closer. Maybe.

I look at the 'sample'. Cold season has really been a help. All those discarded tissues. It took a while under the hand dryer, but I've got what I need.

I wish I could describe the feeling just before the brain dump happens; it's like a crazy jumble of—

'Did you get the Dr Pepper?'

'Here's your cheeseburger, Axej—'

'Sid?'

'And onion rings; you wanted onion rings, right?'

'Sid...'

'There's an extra napkin too—'

'Sid! Did you get the Xxyxcing Dr Pepper?'

'I forgot.'

'Xxyxc, Sid!'

'Sorry, I got distracted. There was a woman dressed as a cat.'

'Every time, Sid, every exxxy time.'

'I know. I'm really sorry.'

Pause.

'How many so far?'

'We managed one hundred this morning.'

'There's like a hundred thousand people here, and we've given away one hundred?'

'Sid, don't start - I told you this was a crap location.'

'No you didn't!'

'Yes, I did—'

'No, you said by the stairs.'

'I said we'd be better off near the Star Wars booth.'

'You said by the stairs, lots of foot traffic—'

'Well naturally, once you screwed up getting the good spot I tried to put the best spin on it—'

'When I screwed up?!? What about—'

'Will you shut the Xxyxc up? You'll scare people off!'

'Sorry, Axej.'

'One hundred's fine. There'll be more people by this afternoon, and—'

'Customer!'

'Greetings, Earthling!'

'Um. Hi. Nice costume.'

'Please take free merchandise.'

'Giveaways? Cool! What is this, a new show?'

'It's Invasion, Earthling. We are your new overlords.'

'Nice! Some kind of spoof deal? Comedy? You look a bit like those ones from the Simpsons...'

'Listen, human, we are not—'

'Yes, comedy. Invasion. Please take one.'

'What is it, USB? There a trailer on there, or something?'

'Computer virus. Will enable Invasion to spread via the network. Soon all your nodes will belong to us.'

'Viral marketing? Very cool. Is it Mac compatible?'

'What?'

'Will it run on a Mac?'

'Yes, Earthling.'

'Are you sure? Because I've had that before where—'

'Look, will you just take the Xxyxcing thing?'

'What my friend means is...'

'Never mind dude, I'll pass.'

'Please! You must aid us!'

'Whatever, that guy's a douche.'

'It's limited edition!'

'Oh yeah?'

'Only one thousand in existence. Numbered.'

'Huh.'

'Will serve as token of honour when Invasion is complete.'

'Oh, yeah? What is that, like, priority sales or something?'

'It means we will eat you last.'

'Ha! Good one, you're really in character, I like it.'

'So, you take, Earthling.'

'Well...could you guys sign it, or something?'

'Sign it? Can you see my appendages? How'm I supposed to hold an Xxyxcing pen?'

'Hey, forget it. You know, you're an asshole, I hope you—'

ZAP.

Pause.

'Xxyxcing hell, Sid!'

'It was compromising the mission! It would've talked!'

'Seriously?'

'I'm tellin' you...'

'Sid? Xxyxcing seriously?'

'I'm telling you, it was a threat...'

'Oh, yeah, course it was. "I saw two aliens at the sci-fi convention, they told me they were going to try and take over the world." We'd have been right up the axxalbx canal then, wouldn't we?'

'...'

'What, Sid? What?'

'Wasn't gonna take one anyway.'

'Oh, and that's the point, is it?'

Pause.

'Sid?'

'Yeah?'

'Get the Xxyxcing DustBuster, clear up that mess, OK? Also, and I really can't emphasise this enough, right? NO MORE DISINTEGRATIONS. The next time you do, you'll be on mite-eating duty for a month when we get back to the ship. Understood?'

'Yeah.'

'Good.'

Pause.

'How much longer?'

'Seven hours.'

'Xxyxc!'

Pause.

'I hate this Xxyxcing planet.'

...Fuck! I guess that setting I fiddled with affects the visual input - it was like being blind. I'll need to change that for—

Wait, *what?*

<INPUT ENDS>

<INPUT BEGINS>

I may just have uncovered The Big One: the origin of The Information War! This is terrifying.

We know so little. Obviously. To maybe have a big piece of the puzzle just fall into my lap...

I don't know who you are yet. I haven't figured it all out, but I think I have to acknowledge at this point that I'm creating this record for someone. Because this machine, the outputs, this record *has to be* made public. I may not survive this. They may kill me if they find out. Probably will, in fact. Somehow, this information has to survive me. It has to make it out there. To you, whoever you are.

Because this machine is reclaiming our history. And I want it all back. Not just for me. For you, too.

I am so afraid.

<INPUT ENDS>

<INPUT BEGINS>

Picked up three more tissues in the last few days. Have to be more careful though – my Protocol Officer almost spotted me taking the last one from the waste. Got to be smarter; this is not a game.

That last dump is haunting me. If only I hadn't messed with the inputs, I could actually have seen the creatures that started this whole thing. I could have seen The Enemy.

We know nothing about them. We only know the holes they left – in our cities, in the earth, and of course, in our understanding of ourselves; the loss of history, of knowledge. We know we won. We must have! We're here, they're not.

<Are you sure about that?>

But how we won, what weapons we used to defeat them, what they wanted...it's all gone.

That machine data output is the first contact we've had with The Enemy in...well...there's no way of knowing, is there?

No clue.

Anyway.

Machine re-calibrated, sample loaded. Let's see what—

It's 10.20 a.m. and John is under the truck. It's safer there, honestly. Out in the garage, they've gathered, waiting for the shipment to arrive, shooting the shit. Good guys, no question, but on the other hand, tempers have been known to fray on a wait, and John knows he's an easy target for some ragging, and he'd just as soon not. His head is still pounding from the drunk he was on last night (exacerbated by Hattie's not-at-all subtle scolding for forgetting Valentine's Day. Lord, could that woman yell when she wanted to, God love her and keep her, but Christ!). His hands are a little shaky too, truth be told, but he can still hold his tools and the work itself is soothing in its familiarity. Yes, under the truck is definitely best. He can work, and while he's working, he can listen in on the guys yakking.

That too is soothing in its familiarity.

'...so I'm like, hey, I don't give a fuck what the sisters told you, I want what I want, ya dumb skirt! I put out for the meal, now you put out for me or I'll knock your fucking teeth out and do it anyway!'

There's a roar of laughter at this, troll-like.

'So did she go for it?'

'Fucking-A she did, that's what I'm saying. These dumb broads, they're all dirty underneath – just gotta give 'em a bit of encouragement sometimes, see?'

'What, in the fucking car park, she fucking did it?'

'No, I took her home, got her to do it in front of the kids. What the fuck do you think, ya mook?' More laughter. 'Yeah, in the car, out back of the club. Did pretty good for a first timer. Thought she was gonna gag at the end, 'till I told her anything she got on the upholstery she was fucking licking off.'

Another roar, this one sustained. At least one of them seems to be struggling for breath, choking.

'Actually Frank, that's kinda what *she* sounded like. Were you there or something?'

John grins to himself under the truck, work forgotten. Pete is such a funny fucker – always ragging his brother like that.

'You weren't hiding in the trunk again, were you? Jerking off like usual? I fucking told you about that shit, Frankie. Jesus Christ...'

'Hey!' The voice is deeper, craggy, and carries an unmistakable note of authority. 'Don't blaspheme, Pete. Told you about that shit.'

'Shit, sorry Jimmy, I fucking forgot myself. Sorry.'

Silence. John's grin fades. Jimmy has a way of doing that to a conversation. Still, he is Bugs' second, and that's not a job you get just for showing up. He's earned his place and then some, and if he says shut it, it shuts.

Feet shift. Someone lights a cigarette.

'Fucking time you got?'

Pause.

'Ten twenty-two.'

'They said half ten, Jimmy?'

'That's the word.'

More silence.

'We waitin' on anyone?'

'Al's meant to be here. Bugs is coming for the sale.'

'Fucking Al. That chump'll be late for his own fucking funeral.'

'Well, he knows the meet is half past. If Bugs gets here and Al ain't made it...'

'Why in the fuck is Bugs coming anyway? Don't he trust us?'

'Not about us.' Jimmy again. Calm, in control. Almost smooth. 'New supplier. Two trucks of Old Log Cabin. Fifty-seven bucks a case. Good deal, right, Adam?'

'Yes, sir. We should be able to flip it easy.' High voice. Nervous. This is a little closer to the front line than Adam really likes to get, thinks John. His world, behind the desk, is a lot safer than meets to pick up bootleg liquor in a garage, even if it is, in fact, 'the good stuff'.

'As long as it's good.' Jimmy again. 'Bugs'll make sure it's not bathtub gin and tea. Sends a message. Either way. Which reminds me, check your pieces. Don't want anyone caught with their dick in their hands if this does go south.'

More laughter at this, but quieter, more respectful. Also, a series of clicks and clacks, metal on metal. Sounds John knows all too well; sounds that make his weakened stomach roll unpleasantly, bringing the taste of the eggs he had for breakfast up into his throat.

He hears Renny giggle, nervously. Chump probably had no idea what he was getting into when he followed Jimmy down here today. Fucking eye-doctor, pretending to be a mobster. Goddam embarrassment.

Please fucking God, don't turn this morning into a fucking shooting gallery, he thinks.

Just then, Highball starts barking; a deep, throaty cough. It echoes in the garage, noise bouncing off the brickwork, and John jumps, almost banging his head a good one on the underneath of the truck, which would just about have set the morning off.

'Hey, hey, hey! What's a buncha sad sacks like you doing uglying up a fine establishment like this?'

'Fucking hell Al, where the fuck ya been?'

'Fuck you, I got fucking time. Hey, Highball!'

John sees his dog's tail start to beat the floor happily. Dumb mutt. Make friends with anyone brave enough to pet him.

'John, you gonna get this heap of shit running for me?'

'Yes, sir, sure will.' John grabs a wrench and gets back to it.

'Al, tell me you're packing?'

'I'm always packing, Jimmy. You know that.'

'Quit fucking about. Bugs'll be here any minute.'

'Sorry, Jimmy.' Immediately contrite, bravado all gone. 'Yeah, I came heavy, like you said.'

'Good. Man should be here any minute. Be ready.'

'Sure Jimmy, sure.'

John follows the polished pair of leather shoes as they walk over to the rest of the group. There's a lot of 'how-ya-doin' and a lot of shuffling, but John guesses the fun's over now – Bugs' imminent arrival has seen to that. He tries to turn his attention back to the truck engine but he's sweating now, despite the cold, and his throat has tightened unpleasantly, tight enough that he can feel his pulse beating there. Six pairs of shoes, and Bugs makes lucky seven, he thinks randomly, and shivers for no good reason.

Highball starts barking again, this time at the sound of a car pulling up out front. Doors open and close, but nobody comes in.

'Johnny, shut that fucking mutt up, will ya? Givin' me a fuckin' headache with that shit.' Al, impatient now, edgy, good humour gone.

'Highball! Settle down boy! Settle down!'

After a couple more booming coughs, he does, for a wonder. Fucking German shepherd. Bark at anything, roll over for a belly scratch for anyone. Useless.

'Hey, Jimmy, you hear about that new cat house Lucky opened up? Up near Garfield? Pete, you hear?'

'Naw, I didn't hear about that, Al.'

'Yeah, I heard he's got all kinda of new cooze set up in there...'

'Not for long,' says Jimmy, and John can hear the tight, scary smile that he's talking through. Not a smile you want to see. Not on that man's face.

'Sure Jimmy, sure. Bugs's gonna take it to all them mooks soon enough. Fuckin' *Lucky*. We'll put that name to the fucking test, and— Johnny, if you don't shut that fucking mutt up, I'm gonna take a fucking wrench to it, I ain't kidding!'

Highball is really going for it now, barking, yelling. John pushes out from under the truck and turns to the dog, meaning to yell at him, but the look of him, tugging at the leash and straining, makes him turn; so it's Johnny, lying on the floor, looking up, who's the first to see the back door open, the first to see the two cops walk in, all badges and blues, guns in hand.

He freezes, immobilised with shock – cops, yes, and thank fuck for that, but it's still men with guns in their hands, and that's never, ever a good thing. Al's already looking in his direction, an impatient sneer on his face, so he's the first to see John's reaction. His expression changes from annoyance to alarm so quickly, features rearranging with such speed and violence that it would, in other circumstances, be comical. His head whips around, hand already snaking into his suit jacket, and Jimmy sees the movement straight away, old warrior, and his eyes flick straight to the door. John sees them narrow in recognition, anger.

'Police! No sudden moves!'

Everybody looks up at that one, the other four men jumping and turning at the same time, and again John has time to think it should be funny – maybe will be, when the moment is long past and he's sinking a few at his favourite speakeasy, shooting the shit – but right now, he can't remember a time he felt less like laughing.

Fucking badges. Fuck.

'Well, well, what do we have here?' It's the first guy through the door, clearly the dominant partner. He's an ugly son of a bitch, John thinks, face scarred from chickenpox, dark close-together eyes. He flashes a big, shit-eating grin, and John notices one of his front teeth is missing. His partner just scowls, gun raised, covering the narrow room, while his partner talks.

'You boys waiting for someone? Huh? Waiting for something, maybe?' Laughing eyes, big grin, but he's looking at each person in turn, scanning the faces, and Johnny senses there's something going on behind the eyes, something bad. His stomach sinks further and he feels nauseous again.

They know. That means this is a proper bust, and it means he's going downtown, and that's all kind of bad for an ex-safecracker who's making a play of going straight. For a second he considers bolting, just running for it, but the barrels of those .45's look fucking gigantic, and the easy confidence of the men holding them suggests he wouldn't have a chance – and jail is better than a bullet in the back – so he stays.

'Now, you're not going to make us pat you all down, are you? Save us all the trouble and just hand over your guns, whaddya say? We're all white men here, right?'

Frank, Pete and Al all look to Jimmy, the same desperate question in their eyes, nostrils flaring and breathing heavy, animals caught in a trap. He shakes his head, almost imperceptibly, then slowly opens up his suit jacket, removing his piece carefully, holding it by the butt, dangling it from his hand like a dead animal.

Highball has stopped barking, almost as though he can smell the danger in the room. As Johnny watches the others place their guns on the floor, he hears a car drive past outside, and has time to wish that he was in it – just driving past this stinking garage on his way to get a late breakfast at Porkies, not a care in the world.

'Hey, you! Grease monkey!' His mind snaps back to the room, as he realises that Gap-tooth is talking to him. 'You packing?' John spreads his arms out, palms open, in the universal gesture of surrender. Gap-tooth laughs. 'OK, get over here with the others, grease monkey. Come on fellas, up against the wall, hands up, you all know the drill.'

Indeed they do, and with the slouched shoulders of sulky teenagers being made to do a chore, they all turn to face the wall – all except Jimmy, who moves with the detached air of cool that says he's seen it all before, and wasn't much impressed the first time.

As Johnny walks over to join the others, he observes that Adam looks pretty scared, and Rennie looks like he's about to pass out – pale, sweaty, trembling. *Got a lot more than you bargained for, you dumb fuck*, thinks Johnny as he takes his place next to Frankie and places his hands up, palms flat on the wall, legs spread. He stands there for a couple of seconds, waiting for the hand on his wrist, the feel of cold metal, and he has time to think *What the fuck are they waiting for? An invitation?*

Then he hears the back door open, and more footsteps, moving fast – running – and the unmistakable sound of a Thompson being cocked, the click and clack seeming to boom off the brick walls, echo in his skull, and he has time to think *Oh shit*, and he has time to think *I'm fucked*, and suddenly his bowels turn to water and he lets loose with an enormous wet fart, the moist ripping sound the only noise in the room, and from a million miles away, Highball barks a single harsh bark, full of fear, and Gap-tooth giggles, and Johnny focuses on the brick in the wall directly in front of his eyes, and tries to picture his wife's face, her body; her and the kids around the kitchen table, but the image won't come into his mind, all he can see is the brick; and then there's an almighty explosion of sound from behind him: a rapid series of flat booms, and he is punched in the shoulder, in the small of his back, his left buttock, he feels the saint's medal he keeps there explode, another punch between the shoulder blades, and he is falling now, all the strength taken from his legs, and as he falls, he turns, twists, and he is punched in the arm, and then three times in the chest Bang!Bang!Bang! and he feels all the breath leave his body as he slumps into Frank. He sees the two killers, Tommy guns on full auto, spraying the heap of men on the floor. The noise is incredible, the muzzle flash blinding, the stench of gunpowder like the fumes of Hell, but he's fading already, the world going grey.

The guns stop firing. In the distance, from the other end of a long, dark tunnel, Highball is still barking. Dumb dog. Johnny makes one last effort to picture his wife's face, his kids, but all he can see is that dumb dog, barking, and then he's looking down the barrel of Gap-tooth's .45.

Gap-tooth smiles, and John has time to think *hail,*

Mary, full— And then there's one more flash, one final booming crash, like a giant steel door swinging shut, and everything that made John a man explodes from the back of his head, propelled by a lump of hot lead, and it splatters like a giant ball of snot against the cold brick wall.

Chicago. Thursday, February 14th, 1929.

...Wow. That was...loud. My head is aching. My nose is full of that burning smell. I can taste blood. My hands are shaking...Shit.

Wait.

What were those numbers?

<INPUT ENDS>

<INPUT BEGINS>

The numbers. They mean something. Some of the files we look at have similar numbers. 'Protocol' says they were just assigned at the file generation stage, randomly. *So why did they turn up in the DNA data outputs?* What's the significance? I need to get back on the mainframe. Run the numbers, the names. Cross-reference.

It has to mean something.

<INPUT ENDS>

<INPUT BEGINS>

I knew it! The numbers - they used them to track days, back before The War. Named and numbered; they used it for ordering time.

It's— I'm not making much sense, I know. I don't really understand it myself. But it's a system. *They had a system.*

Why is this still only on the mainframe? How come the Ministry hasn't released this information? It would help make so much sense of our history, it would transform our work...

Verifiability? Is that all it comes down to? But somebody must have worked this out already, surely...

This machine. How did it end up in that room?

My hands are trembling as I add the next sample. Serendipity, this one – a single curly pubic hair, found in a toilet cubicle.

Let's see what's in—

The symbols swam before his eyes, almost seeming to squirm on the paper. Richard squinted, cursing his bleary *Diablo III* induced hangover. No good. There was a circle, some kind of star inside, but the rest...swirling squiggles in red biro on yellow Post-it. They refused to settle into recognisable shapes. He looked around, sure someone would be sniggering, or trying too hard not to look.

Nothing. Co-workers all heads-down, already taking calls, typing emails.

Bastards.

He peeled the note off his screen and screwed it up into a ball which he tossed onto his desk, booted up his machine, and popped the can on his Red Bull.

Just another day at the office.

Time passed. Richard sat at his desk, right finger listlessly flicking the mouse-wheel. Click-click-click-click-click-click. Pictures of female celebrities paraded past his half-lidded eyes, thumbnails in the sidebar, the actual 'news' stories in the centre of the screen shooting past unseen.

He sighed, shifting the weight of his chin in his left hand. His eyes flicked to the bottom right of the screen. 10.40 a.m. Over an hour now. He clicked open his mailbox, scanned the contents, sighed again. Plenty to do, but nothing urgent. He moved the mouse down to the task bar, hovered it back over the Mail Online.

Fuck it, he thought. I've been here an hour. There's fuck all going on.

Time for a shit.

He wheeled his chair back slowly, easing himself up, conscious of the soda in his belly swilling about uncomfortably. He pictured it momentarily – mixing with the acidic sludge of last night's beer and the two doughnuts he'd scoffed from the snack table around ten – and he felt something rise in his throat, but it just came out as a bitter belch, and he relaxed.

Why hadn't he phoned in sick, like normal? But he knew the answer to that. It was a cushy gig, this IT support business, money for old rope as his dad said, but that prick Derek had started giving him dirty looks during the back-to-work interviews, rattling on about 'responsibilities to the team' and shit, like he wasn't just there for the pay like everyone else. But he'd said something about the annual increment, and a dependency on performance, and Richard thought it was probably bullshit but he'd been playing the new *CoD* for two days straight immediately prior and wasn't in any condition to argue – and anyway it might be true – but either way he'd probably taken enough sick days for a while, and it's not like there's a lot to do once he does get there, so this morning he only hit the snooze button half a dozen times before dragging himself out of bed and into his clothes and onto the bus and into the office, and now here he is; over-caffeinated and hungover but in the office, Derek. Thanks so much you patronising cock, I'm right here, so give someone else a dirty look.

Richard's belly rumbled again, then cramped. Oh yeah, right. Shit time.

He brushed crumbs off his T-shirt and walked down the aisle, looking straight ahead, grateful again for his desk's prime location, so close to the exit. Grateful too for the view, because the end desk belonged to Beccy.

Beccy was a goth chick – dyed black hair, a nose ring. Last summer she'd worn T-shirts and Richard had gotten to see her arm tattoos – parts of them, anyway. They were black and white, swirls and skulls and shit. Pentagrams. So fucking sexy. Dirty. Seemed almost to move as you looked at them. Intricate.

Great tits too. And she liked her tight tops – oh my yes. Tight, and if he was lucky, low cut. He looked up as he walked past her desk, slowing as he always did, and sure enough, the dark purple top displayed epic cleavage. Like a couple of puppies in a pillow case. He barely noticed the thin bandage on her lower arm, the fresh dark ink beneath; his eyes were locked on her chest, oblivious to her disgusted glare, unaware that she'd noticed him at all, so it was a nasty shock to him as he turned the corner, and the filing cabinets cut that great view off, to hear her mutter something under her breath.

He managed not to stop walking, managed to hold in his reaction, not wanting to give her the satisfaction. He hadn't heard what she'd said, exactly, but the tone was unmistakable and he felt the beginnings of an erection wilt in his trousers. Felt his cheeks burning.

Bitch.

There was an answering sympathetic laugh from Lisa, the flat-chested horse face, and Richard felt his blush deepen.

Fucking dumb sluts. Laughing at a man for doing what comes naturally. Flaunting it in his face like that. Fucking shameless. Disgraceful.

You know they want you to look, or they wouldn't dress like that. Fucking right.

He strode into the bathroom, banging the door open in anger. The lights flickered on, automatic, so Richard knew he was alone.

Good.

Richard hated shitting when other people were in the room. It wasn't that he couldn't. It was just the thought of other people hearing him go, listening to him fart and strain, the splash of the water as it dropped—

Fuck that.

So Richard stepped into his usual cubicle (far corner, burned out element, nice and dingy), hung his jacket on the hook, locked the door behind him, undid his belt, dropped his trousers and boxers, and sat.

He could feel his belly rumbling again, cramping, but he did not push. Fuck it. He was in no hurry. His eyes stared at his jacket hanging on the back of the door.

He turned his mind back to Beccy and her great cleavage. He wondered what those boobs felt like to squeeze. To bite. She'd like that. He could tell. The look and the tattoos and the tits-out tops – yeah. Beccy would like it rough, he thought.

He imagined getting her into the store cupboard, following her...no, pushing her in as she went past. Throwing her through the open door, diving in and closing the door behind them, before anyone else saw.

Richard's hard-on returned with a vengeance, poking him in the belly as his mind wandered.

Yeah, push her in. Maybe she even falls over, onto her knees. Looks up at him, eyes a little hurt, a little scared. Cleavage heaving. He'd just undo his belt and fly, no fucking about, just get it right out in her face.

Richard's cock began to throb, hangover be damned.

Yeah, just get it out, tell her what he wanted her to do. Just tell her to do it, even. And if she said no? If she tried to resist? What was it that Borat dude said when he grabbed Pam Anderson in that funny-as-fuck movie?

'Consent not necessary,' Richard said, dopey grin on his face. He had no idea that he'd spoken out loud. He reached out for the toilet paper, peeled himself off a big wedge, left hand closing over his dick, while in his mind's eye he saw Becky on her knees, his hand clamping the back of her neck, pushing her face into the floor hard, while the other reached up her dress to rip off her pants...

His belly cramped again; hard.

Fuck.

He looked down at his hard on sitting snug and hungry inside his fist.

'To be continued,' he said before letting go, allowing the images to fade in his mind as he bore down.

He pushed gently at first, conscious that what came out was likely to be a bit loose, not wanting to blow off a damp ripping fart that would spray the bowl.

Nothing came. He felt something...substantial. Solid. Which was a relief, really, a welcome surprise. Except it didn't feel like it had moved much at all.

He pushed harder, sitting forward a little. He felt something shift a little, settle back. No question now – this was a big one. *OK, time to make a brown baby,* he thought, and pushed really hard, arms pressed into his thighs. He felt it shift again, moving into place, and as it shifted, it felt like it was getting even larger. He knew it was just that the space it was moving into was narrower, but it was unsettling just the same, and when he finished straining, he realised with alarm that he'd simply lodged it behind his arsehole.

He felt a flutter of unease then, bringing with it a return of his earlier nausea. It felt very big, and very heavy. He realised that this was likely to be uncomfortable. Perhaps even painful. *Still, what am I going to do, not shit?* He laughed at his own joke, but his laugh was shaky, wobbly. The sound of the false bravado rang in his ears, mocking him.

He gritted his teeth, took a couple of deep breaths. *Fuck it. The only way out is through.* True, and it steadied his nerve a little. Enough. He took a third deep breath, filled his lungs then leaned forward, replanted his hands and pushed as hard as he could, meaning to clear the blockage in one clean go. Get it done and over with.

He felt it moving, approaching his anus, and holy fuck it felt big, *huge* even, but shit is shit, he thought as he carried on straining, face flushing with the effort, jaw clamped shut. He felt the muscles down there pushed open finally, and he felt them stretch and stretch, and still the thing was getting wider, and he strained and forced and sweated, his arsehole sending up shooting pain until it became a circle of agony, burning worse than any runny-curry belly, and he clenched involuntarily, intending to cut loose what he'd gotten out and force the rest back, regroup— maybe even check for blood, because *fucking hell…*

The muscle of his anus contracted, gripping the thing tight. A wave of pain, deep, vital, rolled up into his belly, and he gasped with shock at it, tears forced into his eyes.

His hands flew out, banging hard into the walls on either side. The thing was solid, utterly unyielding, and his arse refused to believe it, gripping tighter in panic, and each clamp sent another wave of pain through him, bigger and scarier than the last. He felt his breath driven from him, the pain like a band across his stomach.

He was too winded to scream, and made instead a horse damp barking noise that he barely recognised as his own voice. His hands were pushing out full strength to each side, and he could feel strain in his shoulders and arms, but it was a gnat bite next to the ripping feeling in his guts. He felt the nausea in his belly combine with the fear and the pain, drew in a half breath, and vomited. The stench of coffee and stomach acid filled his face as the jet of fluid flew from his throat, spattering over his hanging jacket. He was flung forwards by the motion, hard enough to bash his head, smearing the vomit across his forehead and hair as the rest of his stomach came up, coating his shoes and socks, and pulling his jacket from the hook in the process.

The retch was a full belly cramp, instant ejector, and his whole body clenched with the effort. He felt the thing that was hanging out of him move a little farther, forcing him wider, and he felt something ripping. The blow on the head, the lack of oxygen, and the extra wave of savage pain sent spots in front of his eyes, and the dim and fractured view of the world through his tears began to turn grey, to fade around the edges.

I'm passing out, he thought, dull surprise giving way to panic, and the panic sent adrenaline surging into him, snapping him upright like a puppet being yanked. He swayed drunkenly in his seat, eyes trying to focus on the back of the bathroom door. He clearly saw a lump of partially digested doughnut – sliding down the plastic finish. Beneath it, fresh graffiti drawn in black marker pen swirled before his watering eyes. The acidic smell/taste in his nose and throat assaulted him suddenly, and he felt his now-empty stomach roll again, but survival instincts kicked in and he held it down, unaware that he'd begun to whimper; only vaguely aware that tears were streaming down his cheeks.

He panted, six quick breaths, and the nausea retreated. He slowly opened his eyes again, this time making sure they stayed unfocussed, while he tried to assess what was going on with his ass.

He realised that the near-faint had caused his arsehole to stop trying to contract, which he saw as A Good Thing. The whatever-the-fuck was still lodged very painfully in place, and he could feel the muscle surrounding it burning in stretched agony. He was sure he must be bleeding, but some instinct told him it would be a Very Bad Idea to try and look.

The urge to clench his anus again was almost overwhelming; instinctive. He gritted his teeth, really grinding his molars together in an effort not to. He thought if he started that again, he would probably not be able to stop, and he also thought that the pain would likely take him completely if it did happen again, but god-fucking-dammit the instinct was almost overwhelming anyway.

He panted, face dripping with sweat, mind racing. Could he reach it with his hands? Pull it out? The thought made him shudder, which made his arse twitch, which sent a fresh spike of pain, big and deep and red, right into his stomach. He exhaled with a wounded animal groan.

The only way out is through. The thought bubbled up again before bursting like a firework across his mind. It was terrifying. He felt himself shrink back from it, mind scrabbling for an alternative, a way out, but the memory of that last stab of pain was vital and mutely compelling.

Do or die.

He pushed his arms back into the walls and began to pant deliberately, attempting to flood his body with oxygen, building up to a deep breath that he planned to hold until the thing passed or he did. His eyes regained focus while he did so, returning to the pen marks on the door. Still the pattern swirled, eluding his focus. He realised with a start that it was the same as the weird shapes that were on the post-it note. He felt nausea rise again. His mind flashed to Beccy, that low voice as he'd passed. The fresh pattern of dark ink under the bandage. His heart was really hammering now, pounding sweat out painfully. What had she said to him? *Old dick? Cold prick?* The peal of female laughter in reply. The shame of being mocked. He panted, anus strained and bleeding, building to what he knew would be his last push, and he replayed the moment over and over, trying to find some sense, the words inside the half heard sounds, and it came close then skipped away, and all of a sudden he was out of time, feeling himself getting light-headed again.

Now or never.

He braced hard with his arms, drove his teeth together, tucked his tongue behind them, screwed his eyes shut, and took in a deep breath.

He pushed as hard as he could, every muscle bearing down, straining. The pain bit deep and savage and didn't let go. Tears squirted from his eyes, and he was dimly aware that he was growling with his exhaled breath. Sweat popped all over his body. His head trembled with the force, and he felt the thing moving, each millimetre taking its payment in agony. He felt the ripping happening again, his arsehole but also *inside*; fragile tissue torn open by the passage, nerve-endings screaming. The pain spread, becoming diffuse but still raw, and his growl became a scream but he kept pushing, locked in. He could already tell it wouldn't be enough; the thing was too big, moving too slowly, but he also knew the pain was too great, that this was it, so he pushed on, sheer fuck-you bloody-mindedness obliterating all other consideration, somehow holding the agony at bay.

Just after the point of certain failure, he felt the thing accelerate, gravity finally coming to his aid. It still felt huge, still tore – he was feeling shredded down there now, ripped open – but it moved quicker. He pushed even harder, black flowers blooming in his closed eyes, felt the world begin to pull away and go dim, but the searing pain kept him clawing onto consciousness.

It hit the water hard and heavy, and he felt the splash-back coat the underneath of his thighs. The moment it left him, he slumped, collapsing like a rag doll, the strength drained from his arms. He slid sideways off the bowl, head cracking against the wall. His arse hit the ground hard, and the pain was terrible and complete. It rolled up his whole body, obliterating consciousness.

He lay, half curled around the toilet bowl, as blood pooled underneath his naked torso.

The body was discovered an hour later. Richard was declared dead at the scene, lying milk pale in a pool of what was by then over half of his body's supply of blood.

An eagle-eyed paramedic spotted the contents of the toilet bowl, and the Police were called. It was taken with care, tagged and bagged, and was the principle piece of evidence at the inquest.

The final verdict was 'death by misadventure.' The coroner never commented on it publicly but sometimes, amongst friends, when in his cups and asked with that disturbing, hungry curiosity about the oddest case he'd ever seen...yes, just sometimes, he'd find himself telling of the thirty-year-old IT consultant who'd bled to death in a toilet cubicle at his place of work, from what he'd finally ruled to be 'self-inflicted severe anal tearing.'

Inflicted by a fourteen-inch-long, three-inch-diameter, solid twenty-four-carat-golden object, shaped in such a way as to resemble, with disturbing accuracy, a giant turd.

It usually got a laugh.

And in Beccy's spell book, a single-word incantation was circled in black ink, with a small neat tick set next to it.

Goldbricker.

...Erm. Wow.

<INPUT ENDS>

<INPUT BEGINS>

It's really frustrating, the randomness of the outputs. I mean, I guess they all have a level of intensity in common,

<Not to mention a certain puerile morbidity...>

so maybe that's how they got encoded into the DNA in the first place, but still... Why these particular slices of history? How does the machine select them? And why only one per sample?

I did more poking around in the mainframe. Verified the DNA output from before – the one with all the shooting. Something called 'The Saint Valentine's Day Massacre,' apparently. It was famous enough at one point to be reported in multiple locations, but of course because we don't know how to cross-reference the data by their 'dating' system - or, well, at least, we *didn't* know - it's all just sitting there as part of the 'unverified' pool. This shit is so frustrating.

I am going to *have* to figure out a way to use this information. Some way to get it to you, whoever you are. It's driving me crazy, all the time we're wasting...

Argh. Anyway. Next sample. Another used tissue. Another slight calibration adjustment to the controls. Trying to compensate for the distancing effect without losing visuals. I'd kill for a glance at a user manual for this thing.

Anyway. Let's see what we can—

There are times when my rage cannot be adequately expressed in 140 characters. Welcome.

As I write, it's 7.30 on a Friday morning. It's a holiday and yet here I am, awake. 'Good' my ass. Baby Gonzo, who goes by toddler Gonzo these days, is absorbing the animated *Mr Bean* show the way I used to absorb *Tom and Jerry*, and that would normally be my cue to 'rest my eyes' on the sofa until she starts grumbling for food.

But I can't. I can't, because my brain won't leave this shit alone. Two days ago, I was watching *BBC News 24* before bedtime. Following the 10 p.m. bulletin, instead of being regaled with the local snooze (Dog Bites Man, Tree Falls Over, Granny Laughs etc.), we get a sneak peek at tomorrow's papers, and to assist us in this task, two guests have picked out particular articles for our interest. So far, so what? Well the guests were Jennie Bond and Richard Madeley, and within about 30 seconds, I was driven to a vein-popping rage not normally experienced outside of *Question Time* with Nigel Farage, or Tesco on a Saturday afternoon.

As I noted on Twitter the following morning, it was like *Dumb and Dumber*: current affairs edition, but that doesn't really convey the full horror of the situation. If I say it was more akin to the death of satire, I'm perhaps getting closer – a hypothetical UK version of the *Daily Show* could probably just run this tape, then turn out the lights and send everybody home.

Oh right, what happened? Well, lead story in the tabs was 'girl killed by dogs.' Pretty horrible story. The Mail, of course, is mainly pissed off that no one is likely to go to jail. This is the point where Madeley comments that 'well of course in fairness, if no law has been broken no one can be prosecuted' – devastating insight there, Dick, that's why they pay you the big bucks – and followed this little nugget of banality with 'The Law, in this case, is actually a dog's breakfast. Literally.'

Literally.

Can your mind even deal with the stupidity of that sentence? Can it? Tell me, I beg ya. Because for me, some part of my brain shorted out with a surge of fury that has yet to fully abate. LITERALLY?!?!?!!? The Dangerous Dogs act has been used as fodder for the morning meals of canines, has it?!? Does that, perchance, explain why they are hungry enough to eat teenager? Or could it possibly be, Madeley, that you don't understand what a simple word like literally actually fucking MEANS?!?!?

Is that it? Or do you have such appalling taste that you

were actually attempting to say that the law had made a 'dogs breakfast' of a teenage girl? Either way, you are quite the most appalling twunt. And as if to confirm his fuckwittery beyond reasonable doubt, Jennie Bond describes the law as 'an ass' in the next exchange, only for Mr Madeley to claim that's what HE'D said in his closing remarks on the subject. No, Dick, you didn't. You said the law was a dog's breakfast. LITERALLY.

Jizzbrain.

Jennie Bond, perhaps feeling out douche-bagged and eager to reassert her own dick-brain credentials, came out strong against foreign aid. When pressed by the actual news professional in the room on the proposition that foreign aid was the sign of a civilised nation, her reply was 'I agree, but we just can't afford it.'

Again, I invite you to take a moment to think about that one. Really roll it around the palate of your own opinion, and see if there's a single part that doesn't respond with fury, outrage, disbelief. Is there enough WTF in the world? Tell you what Jennie, my new policy is confiscate the goods and wealth of all TV presenters whose net worth is over the £1 million mark, eat them, and sell their children into slavery. I know that's not civilised, but, hey, apparently we can no longer afford to be civilised.

Fucking chinless simpleton.

Madeley, apparently feeling aggrieved that Jennie was challenging his position as person-in-the-room-who-has-the-worst-ignorence-to-opinion-ratio, topped this in spectacular fashion by admitting to stealing David Miliband's notes before they both appeared on an edition of *BBC Question Time* (a spectacle I was spared, which is presumably the only reason I still have a functioning TV and not a smouldering crater caused by my kicking the screen to death in an uncontrollable frenzy of loathing), and closed out the proceedings by informing us that 'the ones he had real sympathy for were the ordinary Cyprus person.' Yes, Dick, or as those of us who bothered to actually digest what we read and hear, as opposed to merely overlay our own bullshit prejudices and ignorance like some awful shit-relish to make everything taste the same have learned to call them, CYPRIOTS.

I tell you something, kids – shit like this is symbolic of the end times. We're all going to Hell. And when we get there, it's dipsticks like Madeley that'll be running the show.

Happy Easter.

...Shit, too close this time. More like a conventional brain dump, that one. Stream of consciousness? But the numbers place it as *pre-war* - day names, numbers; all that.

When, exactly, did we develop brain dump technology?

<Frustrating, isn't it? Knowing so much more than he does. Seeing his stupidity lead him down all these rabbit holes. Still, try a little sympathy if you can. He doesn't know what he's lost. Not like you do.>

It's making my head hurt. Too alien. There's so much assumed knowledge I don't have. Need to stop. Try and think.

<INPUT ENDS>

<INPUT BEGINS>

Okay, I'm going to try to recalibrate the machine again. I need to try to capture more data outputs from around the time of The War, see if I can pinpoint a period, at least. This stuff...it's killing me; I can't sleep, my head's full of these fucking nightmares. And it's not *helping*, it's not adding to my understanding of anything.

I have to get smarter.

I've got two snot samples left. Not really figured out a way to get more. Need to give that some thought too. Also, I'm spending too much time on the mainframe during office hours. I mean, officially they don't track any of that kind of stuff, but...well, I'm starting to think there might be some kind of monitoring going on.

See? I'm going crazy. What would that even mean? Why would they—

Doctor Baker adjusted the framed photo of Liz that stood on his desk, angling it so that it would just be visible to the woman when she sat down. Assuming she'd take the right hand seat. They usually did.

He checked his hair in the reflective surface of his computer screen, adjusted his tie. He looked smart, as ever. Professional. Buttoned down.

Good.

He tapped the touchscreen that lay on the surface of his desk, and heard the faint ping through the closed door. His eyes flicked down, locating again the family file icon, then back at the door, expectantly. It opened, and he rose from his seat, stepping out from behind the desk to greet the couple.

He was tall, well built, and handsome as the photos, with a thick crop of hair the doctor envied. Bruce Tanner. Forty-two. Junior partner in the third largest law firm in the country. Mensa IQ, psychometrics indicated overachiever with perfectionism traits, but no signs of disorder or sociopathic tendencies. Well-adjusted.

He held the arm of his wife lightly, guiding her forward. Ownership and control masquerading as affection, thought Baker. She was a stunning brunette – smart suit jacket, long shapely legs put to good effect in her professional skirt. June Tanner. Thirty-five. Legal secretary. Same firm.

Same old story.

The doctor took the outstretched hand (dry, firm grip, the subtle scent of expensive aftershave) and, smiling, gestured for them both to sit, returning back to the chair as he did so.

'Well now, good news! There are a lot of details to come, and an entire battalion of disclaimers that you are both probably more familiar with than I am by this point...'

They both smiled at this. Legal humour.

'...but basically, the results of the genetic sequencing are very positive. Congratulations! You're going to be parents!'

The relief and delight were palpable. Their hands grasped and squeezed, and they stole a glance. Bruce grinned from ear to ear. June smiled. The doctor thought she looked radiant in her sudden joy, her sparkling eyes.

He gave them a moment before continuing.

'Forgive the bluntness – I prefer to get the headline out of the way, so you are free to focus more on the details.'

'Quite all right, Doctor.'

'Thank you, Doctor. Thank you so much!'

The doctor smiled. Friendly and reassuring.

'Not at all. This is my favourite part of the job!' A brief pause. The doctor tapped the desk, bringing up his notes.

'The genetic match is very good. As you know, Mr Tanner...'

'Please. Bruce and June.' How very alpha of you, thought the doctor.

'...Bruce. As you know, we screen for all known disorders and defects that can still be passed on. We have gotten most such conditions under control, but there are still a couple of the rarer blood disorders that were having a spot of bother mapping out. Still...'

He waved his hand dismissively.

'...nothing for you two to worry about. So, if you don't mind, I would like to run through the specifications. Is that...?'

'Yes, yes of course, Doctor!'

'Excellent.'

The doctor hit another section of the desk, and the wall screen behind him jumped to life, displaying the contents of the PPRD. He zoomed to the relevant section and began to read, eyes flicking between the screen and the excited faces of his patients.

'So, just to recap; a boy was the preference, yes?'

Nods. The mother's – June's – smile split at this, revealing even, white teeth.

'Well, more good news. The split was far closer to 50/50 than previous years – as you will have been told, it is typically more 60/40, with 70/30 not unheard of. So they have decided to just waive the gender-preference lottery this time around.'

They nodded and smiled, but the doctor thought they didn't really appreciate how fortunate they'd been. Ah well.

'Now, dark hair, brown eyes...' the doctor broke off to look at them both '...they will come from you, Bruce. "He'll have his father's eyes."'

Bruce nodded politely. No one ever gets that reference, the doctor reflected. Perhaps just as well.

'June, you have got really spectacular teeth, if you don't mind me saying so. Bruce, I understand as a child you had some overcrowding, had to...?'

'Yes, I had four removed when I was thirteen. Had a brace for a year later on as well.'

'And a good job they did, too. Still, we shall spare this young man that process, I think.'

Technically he was supposed to be asking for permission here, but the doctor found that couching things this way worked better. Let them eagerly nod along.

They did.

'Excellent! Now as I said, no serious genetic skeletons in the closet, and we've run the splice simulation of the exact sperm and egg we are planning to use, just to be sure. So...'

And he'd lied to them, earlier. *This* was his favourite part of the process.

'...would you like to meet your baby?'

They looked at each other again, June inhaling sharply, Bruce's pulse beating in his throat. It never fails, thought the doctor. Even a couple like this, who must know the process inside out, still, this moment hits them where they live.

He felt the bitterness rising in his throat, and suppressed it with a swallow.

It brings it home, that's why. They've gone through the battery of medical tests, the evaluations, the psych and financial probes, the three-month and six-month and twelve-month checks, all the time the clock ticking, her eligibility slipping away, knowing that at thirty-seven the cut off is automatic, no matter how good the medical reports. Had the arbitrary nature of that cut-off begun to chafe? Had they perhaps even signed up to the 'Repeal 37' movement? The absurdity of linking legal parenting age to fertility and life expectancy data that is decades out of date must have begun to take on an inhumane, brutal quality as the deadline approached. So arbitrary. Life expectancy in the hundreds, fertility through the eighties, so why...?

But then what of the whispers that the repeal advocates reduced their odds in the lottery? A baseless rumour, the doctor reflected, but a bloody useful one.

No, most likely they'd resigned themselves to it not happening – they must have known the odds, after all. So maybe they'd already given some thought to what other purpose the spare room might be put to; but then the notification, the lottery win! The excitement, but also the fear. They've already been vetted to a degree, of course, but there're millions on the register, so the really intense assessments – especially the medical ones – don't happen until after you get a ticket. Around 12% fail at this step, either because of some change in circumstances, distorted claims on the initial forms or, most often, sub-optimal performance at a psychological level.

They'll have known that, smart educated couple like this, they'll have known all of it as they went through, answering the questions, taking the needles, signing the release papers; trying not to feel fear, trying not to feel hope, understanding they've beaten huge odds to get this far but could still lose it all, trying to deal with the pressure of that, and now...

Now is the moment they get to see it after all – the fruit of the labour, the reason for all this hassle.

Yes, thought the doctor. This is the best bit.

He swallowed again, hard.

They were both nodding, grinning. June appeared to be on the edge of tears, and Bruce was looking a little damp around the eyes himself.

'Did you...have you settled on a name yet?'

Another glance. They held hands, squeezed once, then June turned to the doctor.

'Jacob. We thought...'

The doctor didn't move, but it was like a blow between his eyes. For a couple of seconds, he was struck deaf by a wave of feeling, losing most of June's sentence.

'...so, it just felt right.'

The doctor nodded, hoping that his smile didn't look as pasted-on and painful and fake as it suddenly felt.

'Lovely. That's a lovely name.'

There was a bit of a croak in his voice, but they were either too taken in with their own emotions to notice, or simply thought that he, too, was caught up in the moment. The doctor took a deep breath as he looked down at his desktop, locating the sim launcher, pulling himself together.

'Okay. So Bruce, June...'

He pressed the button.

The air between them flickered, and then the image of a newborn baby appeared. The image was photorealistic and fully 3D. He floated a couple of inches above the desk, rotating slowly, knees up to preserve his modesty.

'...meet Jacob.'

June sobbed, once, free hand over her mouth in shock. Bruce exhaled sharply, and the doctor saw a single tear form in the corner of his right eye.

Good for you, thought the doctor.

The baby was in profile, eyes closed as if sleeping. The image rotated slowly, allowing the parents to take it all in. His skin was pink and scrubbed, and he looked healthy, strong.

'This is Jacob at two days.' The medical team did that on purpose. Two days was enough for most of the trauma caused by the birth process to have receded – the face unflattens, the head forms something approaching its designed shape. They'd learned quite early on that 'hour zero' babies don't look quite the way people imagine they do, and it can set things off on the wrong foot.

First impressions are so important.

'As you can see, he is perfectly healthy. Some hair already. Good skin complexion. Excellent skeletal structure, solid metabolism' – the doctor was referring to notes; the parents were unaware as they gaped at the sight in front of them, their baby rotating to face them – '...should end up at around six foot, maybe a little more.'

The doctor noted Bruce grinned a little wider at that, and he felt a sharp stab of anger, distaste.

'And as you can see...' – even with the emotional shock, the doctor had done this enough times that he hit the cue perfectly, completing the line as the image opened its eyes and smiled – 'he is a handsome boy!'

They laughed, delighted, tears flowing from both of them, transported with delight, fingers gripping tight. The image stopped rotating, and June actually reached out for a second before remembering herself.

The doctor left the image there for a while, giving them a chance to adjust, to absorb.

'Really brings him to life, doesn't it?'

Nods. It looked like Bruce didn't trust himself to speak.

'Now, what else would you like to see? We can image any age up to thirteen with 98% fidelity. After that, puberty still has a couple of x factors to complicate matters, but I can give you an estimate of how he'll look on his eighteenth that's got an 82% accuracy...'

There was another shared look, and this time June shook her head.

'That's okay, Doctor. We...we're very grateful for this, of course, but...well, we're really looking forward to the journey, you know? Unless there's anything you need us to see? I assume all this imaging's already been analysed?'

'Of course! Yes, that's fine, we do try and respect parental wishes as far as possible. The imaging files will be waiting for you when you get home anyway, they will play on pretty much any device, so if you change your mind later...'

'That will be fine. Thank you, Doctor.'

'Yes, thanks so much, it's so wonderful!'

'Hey, no problem – you two are doing all the hard work! Start getting extra sleep now, that's my advice!'

'Yes! Yes.'

There was more small talk, but the show was over. They signed some forms, shook hands, and were shown out. The doctor completed this on autopilot, mind a million miles away, so it came as a nasty shock when June pointed to the photo on his desk, just as she was leaving, halfway out the door.

'Is that your wife?'

His prepared response, his rehearsed response, evaded him utterly – driven out by the naming. The only thing he had left was the truth.

'She was, yes. She passed.'

'Oh, I'm so sorry to hear that.'

'Thank you.'

'Well...goodbye.'

And with that, they left. The doctor slumped back into his desk chair, hitting the red Do Not Disturb button. His last appointment of the day, thank God. He rubbed his eyes, not really mistaking the itchiness he felt there for tiredness. He felt the misery descend over him like a heavy coat, bringing his frame down, drawing it in.

He swiped the desktop over to personal use, then

activated the back door that linked back to the simulation program. There were strict laws against this, but the monitoring was a joke, and very few people really appreciated the sophistication of the program anyway. Especially with the modification work he'd put in on his own time.

His eyes turned back to the photo on his desk, taking in the familiar lines of her face, her large, bright eyes; her dimpled jaw line; her slightly lopsided, breathtakingly beautiful smile.

Liz.

His breath shuddered out in a sob.

'Activate SP 1701- Victor Charlie.'

'Verify voice activation password and biometric.'

'Password Jacob.'

'Password verified. Simulation on-line.'

The doctor stared down at his hands, tears now flowing freely down his cheeks.

'Dad?'

The voice was high, and a little distorted by the speakers, but it was clear, and the doctor felt his heart beating heavily in his chest.

'Dad?'

Slowly, the doctor looked up.

In front of him, floating above the surface of the desk, stood a young boy. His hair was sandy brown, same as the doctor, and his eyes were the same grey-blue, but the line of his jaw, his chin, his hesitant smile...

'You have your mother's smile, son. You know that?'

The child wrinkled his nose, mock irritated.

'Yeah, I know, Dad. You always tell me that.'

'I know I do, son. Sorry.'

'It's okay.'

There was a long silence, each regarding the other.

'Dad?'

'Yes, son?'

'Why are you crying?'

...Too much. I can't even...

<INPUT ENDS>
<INPUT BEGINS>

Sorry. Sorry. Just...ah, we've lost so much. Life expectancy in the hundreds? Fertility to the eighties? When I think about just the birth *survival* rates now...

How did this happen? What was done to us? How can we have something as sophisticated as brain dump capacity, but we still can't get infant mortality below 30%? We had medical science so fucking good they had to ration *conception,* and now...now we don't even bother with funeral rites for the under-fives.

I want it back. All of it. I need to find a way to get closer. If only I could have gotten right inside the head of that doctor, think what I could have learned, what knowledge I could have brought back.

I need to figure out how to make this fucking machine work better.

I need more samples.

<INPUT ENDS>

<INPUT BEGINS>

Well. Okay. I may in fact be going out of my mind.

Scary day at the office. Protocol Supervisor called me

in. Started talking about strange behaviour, asked if I was well. Never a good sign. I told her I was fine, maybe a little tired.

Then she started asking about my work, the compiling and the storage. I found answers that were factually accurate, but it was a struggle. I was terrified she'd just ask me something blunt, direct, but...it was like she couldn't quite bring herself to. Thankfully. Still, some of the questions she was asking...it's like she knew I'd been sniffing around on the mainframe. But there's no way of tracking individual users – it's just one of many capacities we lost.

Or at least, that's what they tell us.

Because I found something else impossible today. I was trying to verify that last brain dump recording from the machine output - seeing if I could find something contextual, something that might give me a 'date' I could tie it to. I'd found a folder that looked promising, but I couldn't access it.

It was encrypted.

Only that's not possible, because it was one of *our* re-named data files, on *our* mainframe. We don't bother storing encrypted data because we know we don't know how to decrypt it. In fact, it's not even *possible* to save encrypted files on the mainframe.

And yet, there it was. With *our* naming conventions. Created by *us,* which is impossible. And—

...and oh shit, I'm a total idiot. It was after my attempt to open the file that Protocol called me in. She knows. *They* know. Oh, shit, I'm fucked. Fuck.

Fuck. Calm down, calm. Breathe. Okay, what do they know? They know you tried to access a file you shouldn't have even been looking for, which means they're monitoring what you do on the terminal. No wait, maybe not. Maybe it's just that secure files set off an alarm, trigger some kind of response if they're accessed. Yeah, that fits better with the events. Otherwise I'd have been pulled in days ago.

Okay, okay. That's not great, but it's not terrible either. It could have been an honest mistake, curiosity getting the better of you. They must have assumed that, or she'd just have asked you outright...

Assuming it was just trying to access the file that triggered the alarm. Assuming they haven't been tracking everything you do; all those data searches in the unverified files when you should have been uploading like a good little cog.

But they *can't* be. That would mean...I mean...can they?

Well, okay. So I may not have as much time as I thought.

Good job I solved the sample problem. I picture the clear bag of used cardboard water cones, and smile. Sure, there will be some duplication, but I should have twenty distinct saliva samples here, maybe more.

My smile doesn't last long. Better get cracking. I've adjusted the settings, trying to get closer, but hopefully not sacrificing vision this time. So, let's—

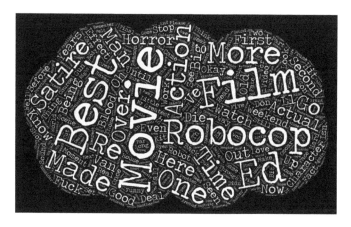

This contains epic spoilers for the film *RoboCop* – as in,

it's likely to spoil your 20th re-watch, let alone your first viewing. For this reason, and because the 1987 movie *RoboCop* is objectively the best movie ever made, if you haven't seen it, go and see it right now, for the love of God. Then come back once you've scraped your brain off the wall and deposited it back into your skull, okay?

Oh, there're also spoilers for *Lethal Weapon*, *Face/Off*, *Die Hard*, *First Blood*, *Don't Look Now* and, in a cruel twist of fate, the TV show *ER*. But fuck them, they're not *RoboCop*.

To describe *RoboCop* as the greatest movie ever made is to make an observation so obvious as to be trite. This is, after all, the movie that set an all-time record when it received 23 Oscars at the 59th annual Academy Awards, losing out only in the Best Documentary category (which is probably the only reason anyone is still talking about *Women – For America, For the World*). Had the film been released in the era of DVD, there is little doubt that a 'making-of' short would have provided a clean sweep. Of course, the Academy did compensate for this by providing the special '*RoboCop* award for outstanding awesomeness in every conceivable way' – as we all know, the only time in Oscar history that the statuette was chrome rather than gold, and for that matter, the only time it wore a helmet and carried a semi-automatic pistol.

It's worth remembering that there was some minor controversy around this ceremony: it was felt by some to be bending the rules a little to have 'Best Animated Short' won by a clip reel of all the ED-209 stop motion work cut together; and who could forget the outrage when the Italian dubbed version of the movie won 'Best Foreign Language Film,' even though the Spanish dub was widely considered the superior article? Still, overall, '87 will forever be remembered, fairly, as the *RoboCop* Oscars.

The other cultural implications of this seismic film event are similarly familiar to us all, so I shall only mention in passing the Congressional Medal of Honour bestowed upon Paul Verhoeven, the Presidential decree that no sequels, remakes, reboots, spin-offs or ancillary material of any description be allowed to be created, lest they dilute the greatness of what had been achieved (the moment when Reagan truly fulfilled his promise of being a unity president, and the achievement he is most fondly remembered for), Roger Ebert's emotional retirement following his simple, two-sentence review of the film ('There are no more worlds to be conquered. Three thumbs up'), and of course the moment in 1988 when, standing in the ruins of the Berlin wall, the ex-East German commissar uttered the fateful words: 'Can we watch *RoboCop* now, please?'

What can your humble correspondent usefully say in the face of the weight of this history? Why, nothing. The most base and lazy student of the past 30 years will already be appraised of the might and splendour of this singular film.

In order to have anything useful to say, we must first...forget. We must imagine. Imagine a world where this film did not receive the recognition it deserved. Where it was perhaps dismissed as merely another late '80s action movie, albeit one with some biting social satire and some good performances. One where, perhaps, Oliver Stone or Woody Allen dominated Oscar proceedings. Further, we must then imagine how that world, that alternate 1987, might look through the eyes of a child...

I was 11 years old when I first saw *RoboCop*.

It was the summer of 1989 – the school summer holidays, to be as precise as I can manage at such distance

– and I was staying at the house of my best friend, Ed (not his real name) for the weekend. 'Ed's' mother was away for most of the Saturday. This was fortunate because Saturday was the day the video van man came around.

To understand the 'video van man,' you have to understand rural Devon, circa 1989. Not a wretched hive of scum and villainy (me and my mates did our best but there were only three of us, and only so many milk bottles you could steal), more a cultural wasteland. The nearest town that had a cinema was 8 miles away. When you're 11 years old, that might as well be the moon. The nearest video rental place was similarly far away.

That's where the video van man came in.

I don't know for sure if he was actually affiliated with an existing video rental establishment, or just a chancer with a respectably large VHS collection and a van. It didn't matter. What did matter was that, once a week, he came to the village, stopping at each house that had a VCR (don't ask me how he knew which did and which did not, but the bugger did – we didn't get one until I was 13, and were bothered not once in all that time, then, within 2 weeks of ours being hooked up, there he was), and he opened the back of the van so we could all have a good peruse. In and of itself, this was of course, a Big Deal. What elevated him from merely Big Deal to Life Changer was this – he *didn't give a fuck about age certificates.* Not a single, solitary fuck. If you were old enough to read the name of the film you wanted to rent, and you were prepared to relinquish the two pound coins he wanted as payment, the VCR was yours for the week, no questions asked.

Madness.

(I discovered later that the situation was even more nefarious. Once we had a VCR at home and he noted my predilection for horror films, he granted me access to the 'hidden' drawer of *banned* films, like *Zombie Flesh*

Eaters and that one where the devil came out of a woman's ear. Had I been exposed to them at 11 rather than 13, I might be recording a quite different commentary, waxing lyrical about the evils of horror-film makers and the warping effect of such infamy on young minds.

Probably not. I'd read *IT* by then. Still.)

'Ed' and I were familiar with his services already, having tested the waters on a prior occasion with the delightful *Big Trouble in Little China*, which had rightly absorbed us for a weekend. But *Big Trouble* was only a 15, and this weekend we were determined to go All The Way. It was time to test our courage and resolve against the big red warning that read: '18 – Adults only.' What taboo could be more thrilling to break? What depraved delights would we find inside? What deeply unsuitable sights and sounds might we encounter: Bloodshed? Dismemberment?

Boobs?

We scanned the library of titles with eagerness and care, but there would be – could be – only one serious contender. We'd seen the poster before, that amazing image of the cyborg stepping out of the police car, looking like the meanest thing to have ever walked creation, and that awe-inspiring minimalist tag line:

PART MAN.

PART MACHINE.

ALL COP.

We paid the man in slightly sweaty pound coins, and took our prized possession back into 'Ed's' house for immediate consumption. It was 10 a.m., and his mother would not return to the house until at least 5 p.m.

It was *RoboCop* time.

Here's the problem with the next bit – I can't do it. I've seen *RoboCop* in excess of seventy times now. This is way more than twice the number of times I've seen my

next most-watched film (either *Pulp Fiction* or *The Sting*).
I regret not a single viewing, and hope to double it or more
before I die, but there is one unavoidable consequence
which is that I can no longer accurately recreate that first-
time viewing experience.

I was 11. I will have liked the gun. I will have fallen in
love with the sound of his footsteps, the robotic whine and
deep bass crunch of each boot hitting the floor. I must
have been horrified by much of the bloodshed, especially
Murphy's execution, and the demise of poor old Kenny
(though I also know that by the end of the weekend I
would watch that same scene and cackle like a loon). The
constant foul language will have delighted me, as will the
commercials – I was too young to fully appreciate the
satire but I was bright and film savvy enough to realise
they were supposed to be funny.

ED-209 will have delighted and repelled me in equal
measure. Bob's fraternisation with a couple of 'models'
will have left me thoroughly flustered and amazed. His
death will have confirmed for me that the greatest two
villains to ever grace a movie screen were Clarence J.
Boddicker and Dick Jones. Beyond that, all I can tell you
is this: as soon as the credits started to roll, we'd stopped
the tape and hit rewind.

We needed to see it again.

We watched *RoboCop* fourteen times that weekend
(yeah, we were 11; we counted). We watched until the
second 'Ed's' mum walked in, and from the minute she
went to bed until we couldn't keep our eyes open any
longer (around 2 a.m.). She went out after breakfast on
Sunday morning, and we hit play again.

We watched it. We rewound it. We slow-moed. We
frame advanced. We replayed lines of dialogue over and
over, trying to replicate the cadence and timbre perfectly
(to this day, I think I have a pretty decent 'dead or alive,
you're coming with me', and my 'Well I guess we're

going to be friends after all...Richard' was perfect until my voice dropped), and sometimes we'd do it just for laughs. After all, when you're 11, watching a man repeatedly yell the words 'Fuck me!' with increasing aggression and disbelief as he plugs round after round into the bulletproof metal chest of the hardest android to ever grace the silver screen (sorry *Bladerunner*, sorry *Terminator*, but 1987 just called to say *RoboCop* can kick both your arses), before he is punched through the glass door of a refrigerator as he fails to flee the scene, is *never* not funny. And I lived the proof of it.

Frame advance is also how I know that the effect on the ED-209 gun was achieved by interspersing frames of the 'flame' effect of the gun firing (complete with tiny flames shooting from side exhausts on the main barrel) with beams of solid white to create a strobe effect. It is *also* the reason that I can report with a moral certainty that in that same scene, as Kenny is being shot repeatedly with high-calibre rounds and his chest and stomach explode with blood, that his tie is actually blown into the air by one squib *only to be blown in half by a second squib within 12 or 14 frames.*

I need those of you with a passing familiarity with how movie effects work (especially pre-digital effects) to just sit there for a moment and contemplate in silent awe the enormity of what I've just described. Think about the care, the love, and the sheer perverted joy that must have gone into even attempting that effect, let alone pulling it off.

Suffice it to say, by the time my exhausted, bloodshot-eyed self had been returned to my rightful parental guardian at the end of the weekend, I was as certain as a human being can ever be that I had, in fact, seen the greatest movie ever made.

But, you know, I was 11 years old. What did I really know?

As it turns out – *everything*.

Because here's the thing about *RoboCop*, kids. Here's the great truth I have learned and relearned over and over again since that fateful weekend in the summer of '89. This film ain't *The Lost Boys*, and it ain't *The Goonies*, and it sure as shit isn't *Return of the Jedi*. What I'm saying here is that *RoboCop* is The Real Deal. It stands up. Over and over.

It is, in fact, the greatest movie ever made...and here's the proof:-

First – it's the greatest action movie ever made. Full stop. Oh really? You're not sure about that? Well, by all means, let's look at the competition...

• *Lethal Weapon*? Please. Riggs fails to take the shot on Joshua. He has a good 3-4 seconds – plenty long enough to start cracking wise before he's snuck up on and disarmed – and he blows it. Compare this to RoboCop dealing with Mr Would-be-rapist. Case closed.

• *Face/Off*? Warmer, but here's the problem: ultimately, the characters are just chess pieces, moved about the plot on pre-determined courses in order to facilitate one (admittedly gorgeous) action scene after another. If you doubt me, consider the entirely superfluous 'oh, I just realised we haven't had a speedboat chase yet' finale, or the nauseating 'hey I lost my son but I will instead adopt the son of my actual son's killer (and also the man who has effectively raped my wife for the last few weeks), and my wife will be cool with that because *that's how people work.'* I mean to say, lovely action sequences, but blergh.

• *Terminator/Terminator 2*? Here's the problem

with those choices – Arnie is only good as a wooden robotic character because he is, in real life, a wooden robotic character. In *T2*, when 'real stuff' starts happening, he's woefully inadequate to the task, and *The Terminator* lacks that amazing moment when Paul Weller says 'I can feel them...but I can't remember them.'

• *First Blood/Rambo*? *First Blood* is a fine, fine film. But ultimately, the 'action' is the least important part, and not what defines the film as important or good. That is entirely down to the closing 15 minutes of the movie, when John Rambo finally collapses into a gibbering heap, recounting fractured stories of fallen comrades and his return home, as the PTSD that's driven the whole sorry narrative finally unravels him, and the broken-down vet from Springsteen's 'Born In The U.S.A.' is made flesh before our disbelieving eyes. A great movie? Absolutely. The best action movie? Nah. Not the point.

Rambo, the fourth movie in the franchise, suffers from the opposite problem. If we were to discuss 'purest action movie,' I think a strong case could be made. But pure ≠ best.

• *Die Hard*. Okay, you know what? This is a serious contender, and worthy of respect. *Die Hard* features wall-to-wall outstanding acting performances, brilliantly choreographed action set-pieces that flow effortlessly and logically, sublime pacing, and supremely satisfying plotting. Plus Alan Rickman and Bruce Willis at the height of their powers.

You know what it doesn't have? '20 seconds to comply.'

'Okay, Kit, you got us, *RoboCop* is the best action movie

ever made. Fine, conceded. But best movie full stop?'

Fair question. But here's the thing about *RoboCop*: it isn't just the best action movie ever made.

It's also the best *satire* ever made. As the following comparisons will amply demonstrate...

- *Dr Strangelove*? Okay, show me the bit in *Dr Strangelove* where there's a massive shootout in a cocaine factory. I can wait...*forever, because it's not there!*

- *Burn After Reading*? I'll grant you, it's got the funniest punch line, but you have to slog through the 120 minutes of shaggy-dog setup to get there. Also, no 'Nuke 'em!'

- *The Big Lebowski*? It's funnier, I'll freely grant, but not actually a satire. Also, at no point does anyone say 'I'd buy that for a dollar!'

But I'm not done there. In addition to being best action movie and the best satire, *RoboCop* is also the best satire *of an action movie.*

What's that you say? *Last Action Hero*?

As the kids say, 'LOL.'

'Okay Kit, you got it. The best action movie, the best satire, and the best satire of an action movie. Sounds like this *RoboCop* movie might actually be a bit of a thing, but—'

But nothing, I'm not done yet. There's one final category in which *RoboCop* is objectively the best film ever made, and it's the clincher. Ready?

RoboCop is...the best horror movie ever made.

I can hear your incredulous gasp from here. I think I may even detect some indignant spluttering, perchance the odd harrumph. But please, consider the evidence...

- *Don't Look Now*? All chat, no trousers. Ooh, a little person in a red coat! Big deal.

- *The Texas Chainsaw Massacre*? This movie has a killer rep but it's a smokescreen. Body count talks, BS walks. So long, Leatherface.

- *The Exorcist*. Again, it's a good horror movie. But where is the moment in *The Exorcist* when a man drives into a vat of toxic waste, tumbles from the rear of his van, shuffles up to a colleague with his skin *actually melting off his body* while gibbering 'hellllll me!' (only to be rejected by said colleague and ultimately killed by being hit by a speeding car that is going so fast that the weakened state of the body causes, on impact, the head to roll over the roof of the car as the legs collapse underneath and blood washes over the windscreen?)

   Fucking nowhere, that's where.

Sidebar: as well as the aforementioned death by toxic waste in *RoboCop*, Paul McCrane would go on to play Robert Romano, by far the most interesting character in the entire 734 season run of *ER* (*Ed: Is this right? Kit: It felt that long...*) This character would lose a hand to a freak accident with a helicopter, and later die by having that same helicopter *dropped on his head*. Thanks to *RoboCop*, that remains only the second strangest death this actor has had a character suffer from.

For that shit, you need *RoboCop*. You also have:

- Metal fist spikes driven through necks.

- Visceral body shock horror – Murphy's execution

scene is as brutal and sadistic as anything you'll see in *Hostel*, and with 1000% more point.

● A man is shot through the knees and then executed BY TIMED GRENADE.

● ED-209 shooting an innocent man for over 60 seconds (assuming you have the director's cut) while his corporate colleagues watch, helpless.

● Oh yeah, also, it's basically a retelling of *Frankenstein*.

BLAM! Best horror movie ever. Fact.

'Blimey Kit, that's pretty comprehensive. Anything else?'

Nnnnnnnn—Yes. Actually yes. *RoboCop* is also the finest comedy-horror movie ever made. Because *Young Frankenstein* isn't actually scary, *Scream* isn't actually funny, and *Scary Movie* is nether scary nor funny.

And here's the thing: being the best action movie, satire, satire of an action movie, horror movie, and comedy-horror movie doesn't merely mean the film is five times better than its nearest rival. Oh no. Because those rivals were only trying to be one thing. *RoboCop* tries, and succeeds, at being the best at *five different categories of movie at the same time.* That's not five times more difficult, that's *exponentially* five times more difficult.

I can see I'm losing some of you. Not to worry, I've created this handy pie chart comparison, which I think illustrates my point with greater clarity:

Things that make Robocop awesome vs things that
make every movie ever made awesome

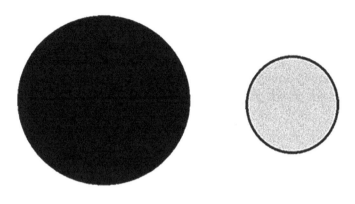

KEY: Robocop • every other movie ever made

There you have it. I haven't even scratched the surface of
the universe of awesome represented in the above chart:
the essential goofiness of Murphy that makes his
humanity apparent and also provides the bridge to his
horrifically altered state; when the gun trick he learned to
impress his son becomes the way in which his ex-partner
realises who RoboCop really is; the hard-bitten black desk
sergeant that rises above cliché thanks to a transcendent
performance by character actor Robert DoQui. The
sound! The sound of those metallic boots hitting the
ground; the background whine of robotics in the
background; the awesome BOOM of the military grade
firepower OCP gives to the gangsters, set loose to destroy
RoboCop; the harsh robotic intonation of ED-209
informing the hapless Mr Kenny that he has 5 seconds to
comply, never mind that fact that he complied 17 seconds
ago and in another 3 seconds will be shot to hamburger
until the robot runs out of ammo because 'the future of

urban pacification' is a flaky piece of shit that doesn't work properly because the creator was too busy kissing pentagon ass and promising spare parts for the next twenty years to care about whether or not it actually worked.

I could go on and on and on and on and on. For as long as you're buying, I'll tell you how awesome *RoboCop* is, and when your wallet is empty, and the bar is dry, and my liver is failing, I'll still have more to say.

Because it's the best fucking movie ever made. Fact.

It's also the movie that made me.

...Okay what the fuck was *that?*

Too many questions. What's a 'movie?' Something they watched, over and over again? A leisure activity? But...the violence? Children, laughing at executions? Murder and mayhem? Why would anyone want to watch that?

I mean, at least I have some more data points to work with - the 'year' is a number representing a collection of days, so I should be able to place this with some of the other DNA outputs, for context. Still...what *were* we?

The format felt more like a regular brain dump, too. In fact, maybe I'm getting close to something here. I wonder if...shit, I don't know, maybe once brain dump tech came in, it started...writing the output data into the junk DNA, somehow? Maybe *that's* what the last calibration change I made has turned on - access to those dumps. Does that even make sense?

<No. No, it doesn't.>

It's also frustrating that I haven't found a brain dump from a scientist or doctor yet. Imagine what a direct feed from Dr Baker's mind could have told me! If only I'd recalibrated sooner, to avoid that strange distancing effect I was getting before. If only I could run the same samples again... Still, there's a lot here to verify – if I can gauge how long we've *had* brain dumps, I'll be one step closer to being able to place The War. This data could help me begin to do that, I think. I hope.

Going to have to be careful though. If they are monitoring what we do on the terminals, it might look...bad, I guess.

They don't like leaks very much.

Also, what the fuck am I supposed to *do* with all this information? It's too much; I need to figure out a way to order it. And then there's verification – what else can it tell me about what we have stored? How does it all relate together? I need...I need to start systematically collating the data that I *know* is verified, figure out some way to get that data off the mainframe. Start building...shit. Start building a history. A real one.

And a dictionary, clearly. The language... What's an actor, and what does 'playing'—

<INPUT INTERRUPTED>

<INPUT CONTINUES>

Erm.
Okay.
Wow.

<INPUT ENDS>

<INPUT BEGINS>

Sorry. Sorry. Right. So...

Okay, I thought I might be going crazy, right? I was replaying the last dump internally and the recording got interrupted by incoming data *without my head being physically plugged in via the jack port.* Apparently brain dumps can be sent remotely. As in not through a wired connection. Just to be clear, because it's freaking me the hell out. For one thing - Who the hell just sent it? What do they know? And— no. No, actually that's enough to freak me out on its own. Gotta process this...

Oh yeah, the new data. It said

<SUB INPUT BEGINS>

Your boss's machine is password protected. Username: sgs73 Password: Buffalo. Look for a file labelled 'Secure History'.
 Good luck.
 A friend

<SUB INPUT ENDS>

See, here's the thing. We don't have passwords. We *can't.* It's *impossible.* Passwords went out with encryption, and we haven't been able to do that since The War.

These are the facts.

<Heh.>

I think back to my Protocol Officer, calling me in. How she turned off her terminal as I walked in. Casually, but...

What was she looking at? Some kind of monitoring?

And just what in the world is 'Secure History'?

Wait. *Wait.* The encrypted file. The one with our naming convention. Impossible. Like the password.

It's all impossible.

<I've got to be honest - this is always the best bit, for me>

They're... it's...I don't have the words, but...there's the world, okay? There's things as they are: what you know, what you can see; Like a machine or a wall or...or a file on a computer.

An impossible file.

But it's like...they...oh wow, yeah okay, it's like they can describe the world but not-as-it-is.

Fuck it, I'm not making any sense, I know. But...I think...I think maybe The Ministry knows things it isn't telling us. No, not just that. It's telling us things that...*aren't*.

I mean to say: we *do* know how to encrypt. Or at least, *they* do. And they have passwords.

What else? Shit, what else do they know that they haven't told us? What else have they told us that is wrong?

What have I been doing? *My whole life?* What even is my job? Really? What's on that mainframe?

What else are they hiding, those bastards? What else?

I've been desperate for time away from work - time to run samples, time to try to create some kind of order for the fragments the machine has given me. Now? Now I don't know how I'm going to sleep, waiting for tomorrow to arrive.

Fuck.

Fuck.

<INPUT ENDS>

<INPUT BEGINS>

It's all true. All of it. I waited until they all went home, dived in on her terminal. Sure enough, there were username and password fields. Fucking password! My fingers were trembling so badly, it took me three attempts to get it right. The letters I typed didn't even appear, just a row of dots. Fucking madness!

Anyway. When it finally booted up, 'Secure History' was right there on the desktop.

And it's all true.

President Reagan, video vans, Richard Madeley, Paul Verhoeven's Congressional Medal of Honor.

<Yeah. I know. I couldn't resist. Sorry, not sorry.>

It all happened, and it's right there. 'Secure History.' I've got no way of capturing it from the mainframe, but I've seen it now. Right on her fucking desktop.

Oh, these fucking bastards. They've been hiding reality from all of us, all this time. 'Verification,' my arse – they've got terabytes of facts, of histories. They're keeping it all from us. *Why?*

What I'm doing here is more important than ever. Somehow this DNA data, coupled with these brain dumps, this file I'm building, these histories I am collecting *need* to get out there. To you, whoever you are. You need to know this truth.

You need your history back.

And I need to collect more. So, let's go, let's—

It takes twenty minutes for a submerged car to fill with water. Seth doesn't even wake up for the first four.

The car has reached the bottom of the lake, but the right-hand rear wheel has landed on a large rock, tilting the vehicle at an angle, so even though the water is coming in via the full length of the tiny gap between the rear door and the bottom of the chassis, it's pooling in the opposite corner from where Seth is. He doesn't see the water level rise up the heel of his boots, the rippling reflection of the torch creating a series of yellow halos around his feet. It takes four minutes for the water to reach the bottom eyeholes and start to soak into his socks.

What he's aware of then, is darkness, and a savage biting pain spreading across his foot. His body snatches the leg up, instinctively, unwilling to resurface, but the movement is no more than a twitch and the boot slips back to its prior position, and the water seeps in again. Seth feels the biting sensation spread to his other foot, and that forces his mind back into consciousness. His eyes spring open, and precious seconds tick by as they resolve the blurry double image into the roof of a car.

Mandy's car.

The people carrier. The Bitch Bus.

He's in the back.

His head is pounding in time with his heart, pulses of dark pain that spread from the back of his skull across the surface of his head and down his neck, forcing a moan from his throat that he is totally unaware of. Each throb blurs his vision, forcing his eyes to refocus, a nauseating feeling, disorienting. His eyes roll up into his head, come back, pupils dilate, contract. The biting sensation reaches his ankle, and something about the feeling of the water encircling him there forces its way through the fog, and he looks down.

The water is dark, muddy. In the beam of light cast by the small torch jammed in the mesh of the metal dog guard, he sees his feet are absent, below the waterline. Swallowed up to the ankle. His concussed mind reacts as though they've been cut off, because that's how it feels – like his feet have been amputated, removed by the water. He draws his knees up in fright, and is surprised to see his darkened boots appear. He draws them up under his knees, and goes to reach down and touch them, to convince himself of their reality.

His arms travel a short distance then stop, held at the wrists. He looks up along the line of his left arm, blinking stupidly, and more seconds tick lazily by as he turns his head and pulls his arms again; feeling the bite at the wrists now, seeing the short length of chain linking him to the thick black metal mesh that separates the back of the car from the front. The cuffs trigger a memory and his concussed mind flashes to the black varnish on the nails of the hand gripping the bed as he snaps the cuff around her pale wrist, his body pressed against and into hers, feeling her naked breasts squashed into his chest, tight enough to feel her hard nipples and her breathing sharpening.

He marvels at how that could have given him so much pleasure. He finds the image, the memory right now, about as erotic as road-kill. Like trying to keep watching porn after you've come. It's ugly. The cold continues to claw and bite at his feet like a hungry animal, and he feels his genitals contract, shrink, withdraw.

Mortal fear is not an aphrodisiac.

He tries to turn his head to see the other hand but it's higher, and the angle is difficult and moving his head hurts, and anyway, he can feel that it's the same deal. He turns his head back to centre, looking down the gradual slope of the floor. He sees the water, still trickling fast through the crack between the rear door and the bottom of the car; watches the water level crawl towards him. Rising. He sees the wrapper from a doggy treat floating on the surface. He stares at it, and the concussion does its thing, and he's back at home.

Rivet gun in hand. Bent over in the back of the car. Looking up at Mandy. It's a warm spring afternoon and the bright sunlight twinkles off the plastic gems in the thick bands of her fake 'Jackie O' sunglasses.

'You understand once I put this in, it's not coming out? You won't be able to use the rear seats anymore. It'll leave ugly holes.'

'I don't care, I need something that'll keep those bitches where they belong.'

She smiles, a flash of white teeth.

'I'm thinking about the resale value of the car...'

'Balls to the resale. It's my Bitch Bus. Do your man thing, man. I want that guard rock solid.'

'Well miss, when I rivet something, it stays riveted.'

She laughs at that. The sound is pleasing and annoying all at once.

The water reaches his knees, soaks into the blue denim. He feels a spike of pain that is just the wrong side of numbing and he jerks his legs up again, but there's nowhere for them to jerk to; he is jammed into the top corner of the space now, and the water is still rising.

The cold attacks his knee, and suddenly he's all the

way awake, focused, realising this is not some lucid dream, some awful guilt nightmare. As the useless adrenaline surges through his system, causing his arm muscles to lock as they strain against the cuffs that chain him to the bolted dog guard, his memory flashes again. He sees Mandy, rolling pin in hand, that strange smile on her face. He remembers turning away from her, then the sound of a mallet hitting wood.

The water has reached his other knee, is crawling up his thigh and folded-under calf, and he shivers for the first time; a huge shudder that travels up his spine, rattles his head against the metal and causes another flare of pain – not enough to disorient, but enough to cause him to cry out. It sounds like a wounded animal. The sound of his own voice, ragged and unfamiliar, sends a spike of fear right into his heart. He feels it lurch in his chest, painfully, then carry on hammering, too fast and too hard. He feels his breath becoming ragged, panting, as the water level climbs towards his waist.

His knees are numb now, but the cold is stripping his thighs, feels like, and he shudders again, feeling his jaw start to tremble too. The water is nearing his balls now, and he feels them shrivel in anticipation, becoming painfully wrinkled, folding the fabric of his underwear inside them, his penis just a nub, and his breath comes out in a shuddering sob as he looks back up at the cuffs. Tears come to his eyes.

The water reaches his scrotum and it is agony, like being kicked, squeezed, and he yells with pain, tears flowing freely down his cheeks. He feels his stomach turn, but it's too knotted up for him to vomit, his body rebelling at the notion of losing precious heat. He's stuck instead with the knot and the pain, as his balls and dick are submerged in the almost-ice-cold water.

He yells again, the shout gaining a vibrating, quavering quality as the shudders become stronger, feeling as though they will snap his spine, rattle his brain loose. He takes a deep breath and holds it for a second, and though it doesn't slow the shivers, he at least stops himself from screaming again. He closes his mouth, gritting his teeth to try to stop them clattering together, and as the water reaches his waistline he looks back up at the cuff, willing it to be loose, on his wrist or on the car.

It isn't.

He tugs anyway, as hard as he can, muscles in his back and shoulder screaming at the stress, the unnatural angle, and the metal gives not at all, and the cuffs bite into his wrist but move not at all, and his breath comes out of him in a growl as the water reaches his navel, crawling towards his diaphragm.

He doesn't notice that the water level has almost reached the torch, is only dimly aware that the shadows are growing longer as the beam of light hits a smaller and smaller surface area.

Instead, he just feels panic, animal, deep and total, rising up from his chest into his throat. He tries to hold it there and can't. It floods his brain. He screams and pulls and screams and pulls, wasting vital warmth and precious energy and oxygen, bruising and cutting his wrists on the indifferent metal, straining the muscle in his left arm and almost dislocating his right shoulder, and the deep ripping sensation of this last cuts through the panic for a second and he regains a kind of lucidity and stares at the cuffs.

He sees the girl, and then he sees Mandy; Mandy after a kiss, Mandy after a hug, Mandy after they'd made love, Mandy talking – that sweet voice, saying *if you ever cheat on me...*

Then the water reaches his diaphragm, and suddenly breathing is hard and harsh and painful and contracted, and he's trying to scream but his lungs don't have the oxygen, so instead he utters a series of short yelps, and they feel raw and painful in his constricting throat.

It is at this point that the water reaches the end of the torch. The fluid flows against the bulb and, with an almost inaudible plink, the light goes out.

Seth's world turns instantly blank. Void. For a few seconds there's the ghostly afterimage of the roof of the car, then that fades from his retina. He's stopped yelping, is now just panting, his heart racing, and he can still hear the sound of rushing water and still feel the level rising as it reaches the bottom of his ribcage.

If you ever cheat on me...

He starts to thrash wildly, bucking and heaving; all restraint gone, conscious thought obliterated, mind a dull panic – the cold stronger than everything, stronger than the world – and he has a moment in the eye of the storm of hysteria to think that the cold is the only really real thing he's ever experienced, ever will experience, and then his mind sinks again and the panic rises again and this time he does tear muscles in his shoulder and his arm as he thrashes and tries to shriek, voice cracked, throat closing down, and the overexertion and hyperventilation and blunt force trauma to the back of the skull all do their part, and he passes out.

The water rises.

His eyes open once more, but he doesn't realise it. They register nothing. His chin and neck are cold. The rest of his body has gone. He feels drowsy, exhausted. His synapses fire, more-or-less randomly, sending fleeting images across his mind. He sees his mother's smiling face. He sees the ocean. He sees Hannibal with a cigar clamped in his teeth saying 'I love it when a plan comes together!' He sees a hunched-up figure walking across a frozen lake, snowflakes swirling in the wind. He sees an Eskimo. The images fade. His eyes do not close, but he faints anyway.

By the time the water has reached his nose, his trachea has completely sealed itself off in a last desperate bid to keep the body alive. The water flows into his stomach instead, swiftly cooling his blood, and cardiac arrest occurs three minutes later.

It takes hours for the tiny fish to access the car and eat what remains of his eyes.

...I can't. I can't, I can't...

<INPUT ENDS>

<INPUT BEGINS>

...sorry. Sorry. Bit much that. Had to make the shivers stop. Took a walk, stood by one of the building vents. The smell was awful of course, but eventually the warmth got through.

This cannot possibly be good for me.

I examined the machine and it looks like one of the settings got moved, just a touch. Maybe when I loaded the last sample? I've put it back to where it was, I think, but now I can't decide whether or not to run another sample. I'm not sure I can take another hit like that. So much pain. So much terror.

But I need to know. And it's not like I'm going to sleep anyway.

Fuck it, just one—

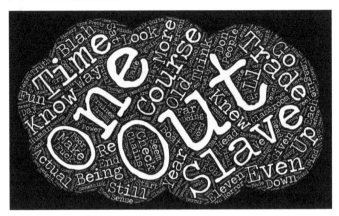

So I'm eleven, waiting out my final year of primary school, and looking forward to secondary school with a naivety that is still heart-breaking even this far out, where, I am assured by adults who should really have known differently, things will be taken Much More Seriously, where I will be Appropriately Stretched, and where they do not tolerate Mucking About in any way, shape, or form. And yes of course that last should have given me pause, but these were respected adult voices; people whose words I trusted implicitly, so I assumed that 'mucking about' meant 'bullying' and not, say, 'having fun.'

Oh, to be eleven again.

So the slow tick-tock of the dog days of the summer term (prior to the start of summer proper) grinds down, slow and sure and fine. That's how it should have gone.

Instead, something actually happens.

That something is a new trainee teacher, who is specialising in drama (the subject; she didn't create emotional strife wherever she went, or at least not in the classroom). Somehow this poor lady had drawn the shortest possible straw, and been sent out to the arse-end of North Devon to teach Drama to a bunch of yokels' and farmers' sons and daughters, for most of whom the height of sophisticated performance art is doing impersonations of what they imagine people of Indian or Pakistani descent must sound like – which are so shockingly poor and horrendously racist that even Spike 'put it in the curry' Milligan would have probably shaken his head and muttered something about taking it too far and ruining it for everyone. And if that sounds like a fun time, I assure you, I'm telling it wrong.

This poor woman. Who exactly within the department for education she'd pissed off enough to get this assignment, I cannot imagine. But luckily for me, she didn't seem to give a single solitary shit about that. Instead, she rolled up her sleeves and dove in with both feet (meaning she got her boots wet, and if you spotted that, award yourself an invisible calorie-free doughnut, on me).

Current topic for our history classes was the slave trade. The head of the school who also ran the 9, 10 and 11-year-old's classroom (yup, two years of teaching in a single classroom, and still less than 30 kids total) loved teaching history. It made sense. After all, if your prime source of pleasure comes from instilling terror into the minds of your young pupils and torturing them psychologically from a position of authority, you can scarcely conceive of a more perfect subject to do it with than the history of our species.

In the 18 months since I'd joined the class, I'd learned about the various torture and execution regimes of kings and queens past. Being hung, drawn, and quartered seemed particularly and spectacularly gruesome, although it occurred to me even then that there was a good chance that – unless you had some truly exceptional fortitude – you were unlikely to make it very far into the actual quartering stage, what with the pain and the blood loss. We'd had the rack and the wheel, we'd had burnings and beheadings. Did you know that kings had to be executed with a sword rather than an axe because it was a 'noble' weapon? Maybe, but I'm betting that less of you knew because you were taught, *at eleven years old,* that this was one of the few times being nobility was a bit of a bummer because the curved blade of an axe would normally remove a head with one clean stroke, whereas even the sharpest of swords wielded by the strongest of men would take several hacking strokes to fully remove the head. You'd be alive through the entire process and feel each blow. Yes, that level of detail. The younger members of the class were nine years old. We'd learned about how certain medieval kings would force people who displeased them into iron cages small enough that they had to crouch, then simply hang them outside the castle walls and let nature take its course. Birds would often eat their eyes before they died, I was informed. The bodies would be left there as they rotted to skeletons. As a warning to others.

Anything else? Oh, indeed. The Dark Ages were a particularly rich source of data, what with the many lethal trials that would either kill an innocent woman or identify a witch (that particular Python sketch never quite rocked my world the way it did many of my contemporaries, I suspect, but that's the power of teaching for you). It wasn't just women who got a raw deal though. Can't decide if you're telling the truth? Plunge your hand into the boiling water to retrieve the stone at the bottom. Assuming you don't either drop the stone or pass out from the pain (both clear and unarguable signifiers of guilt, of course), your arm is bandaged for a week before being unwrapped and examined. If you're healing normally, congrats; you were telling the truth and you get to live, albeit with a scarred and damaged arm and hand. Show any sign of infection though and oh dear, you fibber, time to have a body part amputated.

I've looked none of this up to check it – I'm on a boat,

the internet is £300 a minute, craptastically slow and, fundamentally, I don't fucking need to. It's burned into my brain, horror upon horror, brutality and sadism and mass cruelty. All true, all real; no werewolves or vampires required. Just people, doing unto others whatever the hell they want with no consequence – indeed, with the full approval and mark of authority, which I think is what scared me the most. Insanity and brutality was not just tolerated, it was fucking *mandated.* Good as *1984* is, I think the reason it didn't quite have the universe-shifting impact on me that it did on many young minds was the simple fact that by the time I'd gotten to it, I'd already fully absorbed and internalised the idea that unchecked authority would very quickly lead to scarily high levels of violence, sadism and insanity. It's one of the most basic and disturbing truths about our species, one I struggle with, and fear, and write about to this day. You want to know what Hell looks like? Check out North Korea, check out Nazi Germany, check out Soviet Russia, check out Genghis Kahn sometime, check out medieval Europe. Take a good long hard look at what we do to each other when we let might and might alone be the arbiter of right and wrong. Look it up.

While you're there, check out the slave trade.

As you may imagine from the above, all fertile ground for our head teacher. His particular delight was, of course, lurid descriptions of the conditions on board. We were given the photocopied diagrams that showed the number of people per deck, impossible totals, stick figures arranged like jigsaw pieces, but of course that did little to convey the visceral horror of the conditions on board. But lucky old us, because we had Sir, and Sir was more than equal to the task of transmitting that terror into our minds. The smells of vomit and shit, all evacuations left where they fell; the decks washed down maybe once a week with sea water. Women crying, men calling out for loved ones.

The chains and manacles, biting into flesh, leaving raw wounds which the seawater would attack, inflame, sometimes infect. Exposure to white man's diseases, which would often prove fatal on the voyage. Truly meagre rations of food and water, many dying of starvation or, more commonly, dehydration. Massive brutality and violence meted out at the slightest provocation, real or imagined. The raw terror of minute to minute existence, ripped away from everything you could call home, family, tribe, society; anything you knew or could count on. Chained and floating towards an unknown destination, the only clue as to your final fate being your bonds and the cruelty of your captors.

'Some of them just gave up. They just willed themselves to die on the boat.'

I'll say this for the vicious, brutal, sadistic old fuck – I never got the slightest whiff of racism from him in any of this. Certainly my abiding and overriding memory of the lessons is a sense of gut-level revulsion at the awfulness of the experience of being chained in that hold, and he did nothing to try to alleviate or mitigate that. Which may mean nothing more than his enjoying our discomfort, but it's still not nothing, given the time and place. I contextualise that because of what follows – which those familiar with the work of Neil Gaiman may already be aware of, but which again had a much more blunted impact on me when I read it at 17, because *I'd been told about it in school when I was fucking eleven.*

Because as improbable as it may seem to those unfamiliar with the period and process, there was actually a grotesque punchline to the above, a truly macabre kicker, which was this: all the slaves in each deck were chained to each other in one continuous link. Because for the British fleets at that time slave-trading was illegal, and if they got caught with a cargo full of contraband things were apt to get sticky. So at the other end of the interlinked chains was a huge stone weight. At the first sign of customs boats, the weight would simply be dropped overboard, dragging the entire contents of the boat – that would be several hundred human beings – down to the sea bed.

Profit margins on illegal slave trading were so huge that they could afford to dump six out of every seven 'shipments' and still make a tidy profit, I was informed.

I don't know about sleepless nights, exactly, but I think it's fair to say it haunted me, and haunts me still, given my level of recall on a subject I've ostensibly not thought about for years, if not decades. It's a cliché, but some knowledge, some information really does seem to carry emotional weight, to have heaviness. It's in my nature to want to know, to seek out and to learn and digest and try to make sense of things, and it's been an enriching journey so far, but every now and again you will come across something like this and just be sat firmly on your arse for a while.

Enter our trainee drama teacher.

Because there's a ton you could do, given the subject matter. And let's face facts, most of it would be pretty shit. Luckily for us, we got sent a genius.

'On Friday afternoon, instead of normal lessons, we're going to do a special project on the slave trade. We're going to enact an international court trying to make a decision about whether or not the slave trade should be made illegal.'

To say my ears pricked up would be an understatement. I was mesmerised.

'You'll each be assigned roles, based on the different historical interests involved, and have to give testimony and argue for or against the trade. At the end will be a vote to decide if the trade should be ended.'

I don't know if it was Tuesday or Wednesday. I just know the week couldn't go by soon enough. I was stoked.

I think even at eleven I knew I was pretty good at marshalling and sustaining an argument, but what an opportunity I had here! I started making plans, rehearsing rhetoric. I was going to wax lyrical about injustice, about the cruelty of the conditions, I was going to invoke biblical quotes; I was going to kick *ass*. By the time I was done talking, the slave trade would be abolished by unanimous consent. Probably we'd all get sent home early.

Following lunch, we all lined up to go back to class, my tummy fluttering with more than just the effects of toffee sponge and pink custard. The classroom had been rearranged, one huge long table with the trainee sat at one end, playing the judge, and cards with our names on so we knew where to sit. I remember being close to the judge, and sat next to Sir, who was also participating in the event, but can recall not a single warning bell as I sat down in my place, all but cracking my knuckles in anticipation.

'Blah blah, international court blah blah, gathered here blah blah, interested parties blah blah, resolve whether or not slavery should be abolished.'

Game ON!

'Now, turn over your name cards to see the role you've been assigned.'

I'm not even kidding, I read the word 'Slave', and actually had time to feel a swell of pride before I read the second word.

Which was, of course, 'Trader.'

I remember looking up at the trainee, not quite tears in the eyes, but definitely with no small measure of hurt. Why would she do this to me? How could she not know how I felt? Miss, why d'ya do me like this?

Wise woman. She knew exactly what she was doing. 'I know it'll be hard, Kit, but try.'

There was a final twist of the knife, of course. We were seated by role, so the fact that I was sat next to Sir meant he was the other assigned trader.

It was crushing. At first. Then, as the opening testimonies began, I started to see...possibilities. It dawned on me, quite quickly, that it was possible I could have an enormous amount of fun with this. Because, dig it, I knew where I actually stood morally, but I also knew the now-opposing argument like the back of my hand. As the weight of the emotion of the whole horror show dropped from me; as I confronted the scenario not as articulating a passionately held belief but simply putting forward the strongest possible argument for a position, I realised this was something I could not just do, but actually *enjoy* doing. In the process, I hit upon one of the great truths of acting, and maybe even of make-believe and fiction in general:

It's *always* more fun to play the bad guy.

And I played it to the hilt. I talked about civilising influence, the gainful employment of the ship crews, the appalling conditions we were rescuing these people from and the relatively prosperous circumstances they were being transported to, even as slaves. I flat-out denied the cruelties of the voyage, blaming any losses as a weakness within an inferior species, and you'd better believe I quoted biblical justification for slavery. By the time I'd finished, the girl who'd set herself up as chief spokesperson for the slaves was damn near in tears of anger and outrage at the mendacious eloquence coming out of me (we were friends afterwards though, once the heat of battle had died away – she understood theatre too).

I had a ball. I had a blast. I rocked it and socked it. For one glorious afternoon, I was an eleven-year-old slave trader, and it was some of the most fun I've ever had in a classroom.

POSTSCRIPT: or, What Have we Learned?

Because obviously, as a human being with a conscience, I can't leave it there. Even with two and a half thousand words of context, that last is still a pretty shocking statement. There are two things I want to talk about – one general, one personal.

Starting with the general, I think part of what we are talking about here is the power of play, right? For all that the teacher delighted in traumatising me with the horror of the industry, the one insight that he couldn't give me, the one perspective I could never grasp, was that of the men who plied and profited from this trade. It was incomprehensible to me that someone would be responsible for such cruelty...until I came to inhabit that person in play.

Then, the scales fell very quickly. Because *of course,* if you profit from a system, you'll find a way to justify its perpetuation. *Of course* you'll find a way to render the status quo not merely legal, but ethical; even righteous. *Of course* you'll minimise, deflect, deny, and obfuscate any sense of fallout or human consequences of what you do.

Because that's what power does.

It would be a long time before the concept of 'privilege' would cross my radar in the context of gender and ethnicity debates, but I had zero problems with conceptualising it as soon as it came along, because I'd felt the power of it. Aged eleven, in a classroom of my peers, I donned the mantle of privilege and used it to justify horrific barbarity.

That alone made it worth the price of admission. To this day, whenever I find myself reading the news, or studying some history and I find myself saying/thinking 'I just can't imagine how a person could—' I stop again. Because thanks to that lesson I often find that, with just a bit of thought, I can. It's one of the reasons I write the kind of fiction that I write. Because, with some effort, I *can* imagine why or how a person could...and I feel like those stories are worth telling. Also, because I think the biggest disservice we do to ourselves as a species is to monster the bad people; to claim them as other, as not human. Because no matter how vile the person and how offensive the crime, the hard truth is they are *always* human. We ignore or forget that at our peril, I think, because I'm pretty sure that the only way to truly contend with and ultimately defeat evil in the world, is to understand it.

Know thine enemy.

PPS – We lost the debate handily, by 7 votes to 21, and slavery was abolished (the aboriginal land rights vote a month later went right down to the wire, but that's a story for another day). All the boat crews voted against the trade, doing themselves out of jobs in the process. Which has a kind of nobility at this distance, though I do remember feeling pissed about it at the time...

...'Playing.'

They had a word for it. They *understood* it. Playing. Taking a role. Saying the world is other than what it is. They taught it *to their children.*

Somewhere out there, in our past, there's a classroom full of children who have a greater understanding of the world than we could ever hope to.

Playing at being other things. Playing at...Robocop? It was some kind of...not-real game? For kids?

Is this what The Ministry is doing? Are the Officers all

'playing' - presenting to us facts that are not facts?

What, exactly, *are* we?

<INPUT ENDS>

<INPUT BEGINS> Work is getting more anomalous with every cycle. A new portal appeared on my terminal today. It was called RED PILL.

<Hehe. RED PILL. :D >

I ignored it all morning, but over lunch, I couldn't resist opening it. Password protected. I used the Protocol Officer's details again.

It's a secure area. I can access the 'Secure History' folder. Only it's not a folder, I realise, now I've had more time to sniff about.

It's a second mainframe. And it's got *everything*.

So-called 'unverified' data, logged and catalogued. They're even using the old numbering system - Dating, I mean. *They know about dating.*

I didn't have long to hunt around – I've got an upload quota, and clearly eyes are on me right now – but I was able to find confirmation of the Slave Trade, and it was every bit as horrible as last night's DNA data suggested.

It's hard to believe that we could ever have been like that, behaved in that way. I'm still getting a handle on this 'dating' thing, but it's looking a lot like this slavery stuff happened before a lot of the other things. For sure before the Valentine's Day shooting, before *RoboCop*, and whatever *News 24* was. And obviously, *those* things were in living memory of when the brain dump was invented.

<*Obviously*. *eye roll* >

So, I'm closing in on being able to pinpoint when The Information War happened.

Anyway. The brain dump was right; slavery was abolished – eventually. There was a war, but it ended. At least, as far as I can tell.

Man, this is getting scary. Also hard to keep track of. I need to put it all together, somehow. Get it in order.

Still don't know how I'm getting it to you, either.

Got to keep mining the samples I have left. Let's see what—

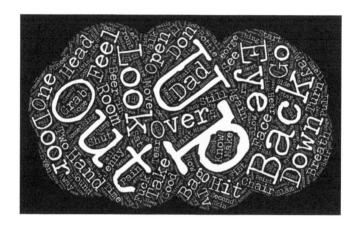

My dad's got a pretty good left jab, especially for a guy who's been dead for two years. He catches me in the gut as soon as I walk in the door, and it takes the breath out of me. I stagger back, pushing the door shut with my body, my hands moving down to protect my abdomen.

The next blow catches me on the cheek, bounces my head off the wood BamBAM! Bursts of pain, front and back. Tears squirt.

'Jesus Dad, what the fuck?'

'Where's my beer, you little bastard?'

I hold up the blue carrier bag, the tins clinking together inside. He grabs it out of my hand. The skin on his fingers is grey, dry, flaky. As he snatches the bag, his smell rolls over me, and I have to choke down the urge to gag.

I straighten up fully, expecting another blow, but he's already turned away, muttering under his breath. He goes into the living room and slams the door. I wait until the sound of his chair creaking tells me he's sat down, then I open the front door again, quietly, and pick up the second bag – the one containing another round of tinnies and my microwave lasagne.

It's experience, that's all. Give him all the beer upfront and I know I'll face a screaming fit around 10.30 – end up hoofing back down to the shop for another round. Also means being up until 3am listening to him yelling at the TV. This way, when he runs out, he'll shout at me for a bit, but when he starts to come up the stairs he'll find the second bag I've left there for him... It's enough to get him through the evening, and means I get some sleep.

I stash the second bag in the fridge for now, nuke dinner, then take it upstairs to eat. I try and listen to the radio in my room, but the TV is too loud. The football game commentary bleeds through the floorboards, making it sound like two people talking at once, having different conversations. I turn it off after a few minutes and just eat.

Afterwards, I sneak downstairs and wash up, remembering to grab the bag out of the fridge and put it at the bottom of the stairs on my way back up.

I take a shower, pull on my dressing gown, and crawl into bed. The TV booms on downstairs. I close my eyes and try to sleep.

Dad got laid off when I was thirteen. I came home from school one day and instead of an empty house, there he was – sitting on the sofa, drinking beer, and watching TV.

He stayed there for the next ten years.

Mum stuck it out for a while after my brother Jack and I grew up and left, but eventually she decided that she deserved a shot at having a life. She walked. Jack wanted nothing to do with him, but I felt a responsibility. Jack was younger; he couldn't remember as clearly what Dad had been like before. He'd been an okay father. I missed him.

So I visited, couple of evenings a week, brought takeaway, talked football. He'd been going downhill anyway, but with Mum gone things got worse in a hurry. He stopped eating regularly, and I got the impression that sometimes he didn't leave the sofa in-between my visits, except to piss. I noticed the post building up, the red letters, and I twigged that the situation wasn't sustainable. The evening I got there to find him sitting in the stink of piss was the clincher.

He moved in with me at the end of the month.

'Hey, George!'

I look up from my coffee, startled clean out of memory lane by the friendly voice.

'Jenny, hi. Thought you were on the 10.45 break?'

'Call ran over. I swear, nobody understands these new overdraft rates. Might as well have put that bloody letter out in Swahili.'

I chuckle, and the sound of my own laughter startles me a little. She smiles back and it warms me.

'Anyway, mind if I join you?'

'Nah, yeah, great.' I point at the chair just over from me.

'Cheers.' She goes over to the kettle, starts making her drink – teabag, two sugars, milk.

'Jesus, how is it only fucking Tuesday?'

I laugh again. There's something about the way Jenny swears that really lights me up.

'Dunno, mate. I know what you mean about that letter though. Been a pain in the arse all month.'

She's nodding as the kettle boils, and she pours the drink. I let myself look at her as she does it, taking in her blond hair, tied up in a bun, the back of her neck above the collar of her shirt.

'Morons. I tell you what...'

She trails off as she turns around. She's looking at me, and I'm so stupid it takes me a second to realise why. By then she's already saying 'Shit George, what happened to your face?'

'Nah, nothing, it—'

'Someone hit you? You been in a fight?'

I can feel the flush rising, shame burning in my cheeks. I hate it. Can't stop it.

'Nah, just fell down the stairs last night. I was shitfaced.'

She looks at me, eyes sad, and I feel my jaw clench. In that moment I hate her for her friendship and her awful sympathy.

'Must have been. Looks like the stairs lamped you a good one.'

'Yeah, innit?'

'You know, George...' There's a lot going on behind her eyes. She's frowning. She still looks sad. Lovely, though. I wish I could help her, talk to her. I wish...but then I get a flash of Dad, hitting me in the face.

I can't.

She comes over, sits down. Normally this'd be the highlight of my day, but her face is still so sad, and I just know she's going to say something – something real – and I don't want her to.

But then she surprises me. She takes my hand. I flinch but don't pull back. The touch is warm. I feel light-headed. She turns my hand over in hers, stares at it, opens her mouth to talk, then stops. The frown goes deeper. She opens her mouth again, and I follow her eyes down.

'Looks like you got the door a good one back.'

I take in my bruised knuckles but I don't say anything. For a second, there's a horrible blankness, no memory at all, then suddenly I remember punching my pillow in frustration, missing and hitting the bed-frame. But what's the point of telling her? Sounds like a lie.

Feels like a lie, even though I was there.

I take my hand away and look at her face. Her eyes meet mine. She holds my gaze calmly, with no front. I suddenly feel on the edge of tears.

'How's your dad, George?'

I manage not to jump, not to look away, but it's an effort.

'Not good. Can't remember anything now, most of the time. Has a lot of nightmares.'

Cover story – dementia. Close enough. Explains why I can't go out the house, don't have any kind of social life. I don't like lying to her, but given the options...

She shakes her head, and I realise she's on the edge of tears, too. 'God, George, I'm so sorry, really…'

'Hey, it's okay.'

'No, it isn't, it's—'

She's up suddenly, and a single tear falls from her eye. It hurts me to see it.

'I'm sorry, George.'

And she's gone. I don't get up to follow her, I just let her go. I stare into space, not thinking of much. Before I go back to my desk, I tip her tea down the sink and wash her cup for her, putting it next to mine in the cupboard.

I don't see her for the rest of the day.

It took me a while to realise he'd died. I'd come in from work, dropped the beer by his chair, noticed he was sleeping. I let him be; went up and showered, heated up dinner. I'd walked in with his dinner on a tray and noticed he was still asleep. I put the tray on the sofa, shook him to wake him. He just pitched forward, fluid flowing from his mouth. The smell was vomit and fermented hops. It was like he'd drowned in it.

I phoned an ambulance. His dinner was still cooling on the tray when they declared him dead at the scene and zipped him into a bag.

Chronic liver failure. No surprises. Well, one: at some point, he'd taken out one of those 'pay-for-your-funeral' insurance schemes, and kept up the payments – or at least forgot to cancel them. Either way, I didn't pay a penny for any of it. He got a good suit, a nice casket, and a decent burial.

I was the only family there.

We buried him on a Thursday. I took the Friday off. It seemed like the thing to do. Was going to clean out his room, but he'd hardly been in there since he moved in, so there wasn't much to do. The living room was worse. I tidied, dusted, hoovered, but I didn't move his chair. Couldn't. It stank of *him*; that was the thing – sweat and rotting beer. I knew I should be shot of it, but it was all I had left of him. It was real, like *he'd* been real. I wanted it to stay.

So I tidied and cleaned and scrubbed, and at the end, the room gleamed. And in the middle of the room sat his chair, untouched; a blue carrier bag on the right-hand side.

Tinnies in reach.

I remember feeling something then – a pain bigger than tears, something shifting in my chest, in my head. I staggered over to the chair, and sat in it.

It felt comfortable. Worn-in. I could feel the shape of him pressed into the old fabric. I inhaled deeply through the nose. Took him into my lungs. *Dad.* The remote was there on the arm. I flicked the telly on to Sky Sports and reached down for a tinny. I cracked the can and started crying as I brought the beer up to my lips, but I was okay with that. *I love you, Dad. I miss you.*

Things went grey for a while. I sat and drank and watched, and cried and drank some more. At some point I drifted off and had a nightmare, and in the nightmare someone was letting themselves into the house. I could hear someone move the plant pot with the spare key under it, hear the lock turn, hear footsteps coming into the house, the front door slamming shut, loud, and still I couldn't wake up... The lounge door was banging open now, someone stomped over to me, a familiar smell hitting my nose...and that let me open my eyes.

He was wearing the suit I had buried him in. His eyes were open and sunken back into his skull. His skin was pink but, this close, I could see the make-up smearing already, the yellowing flesh beneath poking through on his cheeks, his hands. He grinned, and his teeth were the just same, rotting and yellow, and as he leaned forward and placed his hands on my shoulders, his breath rolled over me. I felt myself gag.

He stared at me for a split second, eye to eye, then he leaned back and slammed his forehead into my nose. I shut my eyes at the moment of impact, and stars burst in the darkness. My teeth clicked together. His fingers sank into my shoulders, his grip terrifyingly strong, and he hauled me out of the chair and flung me across the room. I barely had time to open my eyes before the back of my skull collided with the TV table.

'That's my fucking chair.' He sat down as I stared, feeling like something in my mind was ripping.

That had been the first time in my life my father had hit me.

He turned his eyes from me to the TV. Turned up the

volume. Shook the tin I'd been drinking from. Picked up the blue bag, counting.

'You'd better get me some more fucking beers, and all,' he said, eyes never leaving the screen. Then he took a deep drink from the can.

I stay late at the office, not wanting to risk bumping into Jenny on the way out. I stop by the shop, pick up the two six-packs. Then I grab another two, and a pint of Teachers.

Fuck it.

On the way home, I put the whiskey bottle in my jacket pocket, shoulders hunched against the rain.

When I get back, I open the door and just stand in the doorway, ready to jump back, but this time the hall is empty. I step in slowly, pushing the door shut with my heel.

I can hear the TV, loud but not deafening. I walk slowly down the hall. The living room door is ajar.

I push it open with my foot, again standing back, but there's no need. He's in his seat. His back is to me, and he doesn't move. I stare at the back of his head, stomach churning, teeth gritted. His hair is black now, sparse and stringy. It clumps. The smell rises off him, sweet and rancid.

'The fuck you been?'

'Sorry, got caught at work. Here.'

I walk over and drop the tins by his side. He looks down at the clank, and I see him start at the size of the bag. I turn to leave, and he grabs me, scary quick. His grip is fierce and I almost cry out.

'Grab me one out, would you? Pop the lid for your old man?'

I nod, swallowing fast, not trusting myself to speak. I kneel down, open the bag, grab a can and pull it from the plastic ring, crack it open. As I do this he pats me on the shoulder. 'You're a good boy. A good son.'

The can has suddenly become two, then four, then many. I feel my cheeks dampen as the tears flow. I feel my breath start to hitch.

Then the doorbell rings.

I jerk to my feet, staggering backwards, heart hammering in my chest. I feel him try to grab me, but for once surprise makes me quicker, and I cover the steps back to the lounge door.

'What the fuck, son?'

'I dunno. I don't know! I'll make them go, just—'

'Son...'

'Dad, just please stay quiet. I'll make them go, I swear!'

'God damn it—'

But I'm already gone, all but running up the hall to the front door, wondering who the hell it could be and what the fuck I'm going to say. I cover the three steps down the hall without thinking of anything. Take a deep breath. Open the door.

She looks beautiful. The night air has brought real colour to her cheeks, sparkle to her brown eyes. She looks nervy, but also determined, angry even. Her hair is still up and there are beads of water gleaming in her fringe.

She takes my breath away.

'Jenny—'

She's smiling, pushing past me into the hall, her coat dripping. 'Thank Christ! It's chucking it down.'

'Jenny—' Feeling my heart hammering in my chest, breathing heavy.

'I know, I'm sorry. I followed you. Look, I have to talk to you, okay?'

'Jenny—'

'I know, I know, but I just— look this afternoon, I wanted to say…'

She drifts off, staring at my right hand. I look down at the open tin. The smell of lager hits my nose, and my stomach rolls over. I feel sick.

'Starting early?'

I look back up at her, aghast, stomach churning and a sudden stab of pain behind my eyes. My belly cramps.

'Whatever. Look George, all I wanted to say is I don't give a shit how bad things are with your dad…'

In my peripheral vision, I see the living room door open – slowly, quietly – and I catch my breath. My jaw clenches.

'…that's not what I meant, I meant— I mean…'

She reaches out and grabs my free hand, and I damn near jump out of my skin. My fist tightens around the can. My eyes move involuntarily to her face, and she's smiling, but it's a strained one – sad. I'm paralysed; pain and fear and anger building…

'…I mean we don't have to go *out* to go out. You don't have to shut me out, just because—'

I open my mouth, finally, to speak – to warn her – but it's too late. He clubs her on the side of the head with a full tin of beer. I have time to watch the white foam spray out in an arc as it hits the wall, then her head follows, colliding with the plain plaster with a heavy thud. I jump back, and he swings again, there's a loud crack, and her head thumps off the wall again – harder this time. She cries out, and I cry out too. I drop the can in my hand, pull the whiskey bottle out of my pocket and swing –it bounces off the back of his head like Dad's made of concrete. I feel the impact all the way up my arm. He doesn't react at all to my blow, just leans forward and punches her in the side of the head again and again and again, and I hear that awful thick, dull clunk each time. I see her eyelids flutter, whites showing, and I scream as he pounds her. Blood from her split scalp leaves strange imprints on the wallpaper. I swing my own fist, over and over, my blows landing on his shoulder, his head, his back. Our blows land in perfect synchronicity – mine on him, his on her – but he doesn't react.

It's like I'm not even there.

The sound of his fist hitting her becomes damp, squishy. Her body has slumped to the floor and he's leant over her, one fist bunched up in the front of her coat, the other still punching her head. Her face is now a blood mask. My own arm shrieks with pain but I keep swinging the bottle.

'George... please...' I can barely make the words out, her slurring is so bad.

I can feel myself screaming, but can't really hear it. I look at her bloody face as I hit him, my arm numb now, losing strength.

Finally he straightens up, letting go of her and stiff-arming me, in one fluid movement. I slam into the far wall, head bouncing off. I slide down as he turns and walks back down the hallway. Into the living room.

I look over at Jenny, and down at my own hands, clenched into fists. At the glass bottle.

Her breathing has become a ragged panting, arrhythmic. Her face is a mass of purple and red. One eye is swollen shut; the other is bloody, sightless. I look at the split in her scalp, at the hairline. Where he hit her. Where he—

Where he...

My eyes pull back to the bottle in my fist. I take in the lower edge. The blood, beading there, stark against the pale amber of the bottle's contents. Fresh blood.

My mind replays a sound. The dull clunk as he hit her. As *he*...

Sitting in the centre of a small clot, right on the edge of the bottle's base, I see a single blond hair.

I look from the bottle to her ruined face.

I feel something pull, inside my head. It doesn't hurt much.

'George, please. George...'

Everything seems a long way away.

I close my eyes. I can hear her breath start to hitch, becoming moist, bubbly. The sound begins to fade. So does everything else.

...make it stop, make it—

<INPUT ENDS>

<INPUT BEGINS>

I'm done with this shit. Sorry. But I am done.

<INPUT ENDS>

<INPUT BEGINS>

Okay, I'm not done.

I was. I spent a few days just doing my job. But that new portal sat there. Like it was looking at me. Like it was judging me.

I'm scared, but I can't let that stop me. And I can't sleep, whether I do more or not.

The only way out is through, I suppose.

So, fuck it. Back to work. My *real* work. Tomorrow.

<INPUT ENDS>

<INPUT BEGINS>

Learned something interesting about my new portal today. Turns out I can make copies of the data I find on there. The instructions for doing so were in the 'RED PILL' area, in plain text.

Copies. As in *replication*. I wonder how many other impossible things I'll be able to do before this is finished?

Those playing bastards.

I spent lunch pulling across anything I could find in the 'Secure History' folder that linked to what I've been researching – anything that verifies what I've discovered from the machine. It feels kind of pointless at this stage though, honestly. For starters, I'm no longer in any doubt about what I'm finding here – it's crystal clear that I am, bit by bit, uncovering the hidden history of the human race; that this machine is the key to unlocking our past.

<Oh, *crystal clear.* How about you, dear reader? Has clarity found you yet?>

For another thing, it's pointless collecting the data at work – there's no way to jack-in, no way to transfer the data from the terminal off the mainframe into a brain dump.

So even if I *do* locate the timing of The War from digging about on the mainframe, I have no way to bring that information to you directly.

So all I can do is report what I find at work, as best as I can remember. Sorry. I wish I could show you the data I've seen. At least you'll have the outputs I've captured from the machine.

If I can find a way to get this to you.

Fuck.

Okay, next—

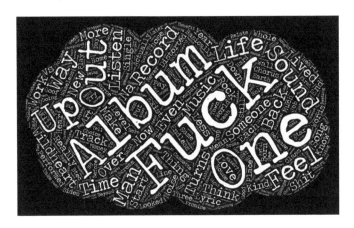

It's 22nd October, 1997, and my life has officially completely turned to shit. Having flunked out of the Foundation Theatre course I had been attending until July (which I only managed to beg my way onto in the first place by promising to also complete the BTEC in Performing Arts which I had flunked out of the *previous* academic year by the simple expedient of doing no work whatsoever beyond the performance related exercises – and try if you can to contemplate how supremely lazy someone would have to be to actually fail a BTEC in Performing Arts), I am no longer an unemployed A-Level-equivalent student. Merely unemployed. For three years. With no qualifications beyond GCSE's, in an area of the country where youth unemployment is scary high, the wages for what shitty menial work does exist is scary low, and where beating the shit out of long haired unemployed youngsters in the town centre of a weekend lingers in that grey area between recreation and amateur sport.

Basically, I am fucked.

Also, profoundly miserable. In all my conversations since, whenever someone (usually a member of the working poor, living for the overtime; pay cheque to pay cheque) starts talking about the 'lifestyle choice' of living on benefits, I think back to this time. I think about how, after my top-up for housing benefit and food and yeah, okay, tobacco was paid for, I had just over £10 a week disposable income. That's for everything: Clothes, toiletries, any drink that isn't tap water, books. And *music*. I think about how, to this day, some of my most valuable-to-me albums and comics are the ones I bought during that period, where every single purchase was agonised over. And I think that it's no more a lifestyle choice than working two jobs because neither pay enough to feed your family is. No less depressing. No less soul crushing. No less grinding.

Anyway.

I'm not just broke, I'm now broke with almost no prospect of ever getting unbroke. I am basically unemployable; I have awful sleeping habits, no self-discipline at all, and the distinct impression that my existence is basically a waste of carbon. I never quite get to suicidal, but I surely bump along the bottom pretty good. No escape route from the hole I've dug myself, no clue what to do to get out. Trapped.

In pits like these, you cling on tight to the familiar. To anything that brings you comfort. For me, that's mainly music. I listen endlessly to the LP's and cassettes that I've hoarded to date, adding carefully to the collections when I spy a bargain, or when one of those must-have bands puts out a new release.

The Wildhearts are one of those bands.

I bought *Earth Vs The Wildhearts* on cassette in 1993 when I was 15, and it's been on heavy rotation ever since. In my own personal pantheon of albums, it is absolutely as seminal as *Appetite for Destruction* – as classic, as vital – and I've picked up and devoured everything they've put out since, including the singles (back when £2.99 would buy you the single plus **three** exclusive tracks so, you know, value for money). Looking back, their latest single sent out some warning signs – different songs on each format was a departure, but I figured they'd gotten stuck with it by a new record label. Anyway, they were still exclusive B-sides, so worth having. But the single was 'Anthem,' and, erm, I didn't get it. On a fairly epic scale. And the rest of the B-sides, whilst more clearly songs as opposed to walls of noise, were similarly red-line distorted almost beyond being listenable to. 'Oops,' remarked one of my friends upon first listen. No longer living at home, parental purse strings cut, that lifeline to new music discovery that was Kerrang! Magazine was closed to me, so I had no way of reading any advance reviews.

But it was The Wildhearts; clearly the single was a goof.

There's no way they'd do a whole album like that.

So when *Endless, Nameless* arrived at Our Price, I plunked down my money for the week with very little hesitation. By God, I could do with a new Wildhearts record in my life, those poppy, punky, angry, happy tunes and lyrics. Bring it on.

And, I mean, fuck. I knew there were problems before I even got home. Opening up the cassette box on the way back, the inlay card had the lyrics printed in it. This was a massive departure for The Wildhearts; prior releases just had artwork and band info, never the words. My mind skipped back to the wall of noise that was 'Anthem,' and my heart sank. I looked up the words, figuring I'd at least understand what they were singing in that fucking chorus: 'I'm in love with the rock and roll world.' What the fuck does that mean?

By the time I got it home, I was really, really nervous. I played the tape. It was the same distorted noise, and also too quiet, the levels way down. I turned it up, way up.

I listened to the whole album.

I went and got my friend – another Wildhearts fanatic.

I sat him down, and we smoked and listened to it, not talking.

When it finished playing, I turned to him. I remember feeling almost choked up, like I'd been mugged by someone I thought was a friend. Thinking about the money I'd spent, could not *unspend*. It never even occurred to me to take it back for a refund.

He looked at me. 'I think that was fucking awful. And fucking brilliant.'

We sat, looking at each other. Then he said 'Play it again.'

I did.

I basically haven't stopped.

I listened. With the words, without the words. Soaking it in. Straining to hear through the distortion to the songs, the lyrics. And gradually, it opened up to me, started to speak. And once it started, it was like a light bulb flickering into life.

This was a horror album.

It was everything The Wildhearts had been to date, with all the polish, the varnish, the love of melody and crispness blistered off by sheer blazing fury and despair. The whole album was basically like 'Greetings from Shitsville' from *Earth Vs* Except this time, there was no escape, no way out. It was the sound of someone utterly trapped, entombed by the weight of their own crushing poverty and misery, howling into the sky. It was the sound of despair so total that it didn't even give a fuck if you could hear it or not. It wasn't a cry for help so much as a primal scream of Fuck You to a world turned irredeemably hostile.

It was one of the best fucking rock and roll albums of the '90s, maybe *the* best. And nobody has fucking heard it, and of those who have, most hate it. That's fine. It's even fitting. But I'm here to tell you that, from where I was, at the lowest point of my life, seeing no bright stars anywhere, starting to suspect the light at the end of the tunnel was actually an oncoming train, this album saved my life. It's not the record that got me back on my feet – or the one that I heard the day I realised that not only could I leave town, but I *had to* if I was going to have any kind of shot at happiness – but it saved me from the darkest moments with the simplest possible message:

You are not alone.

Out there, somewhere, a man you respect and admire and hero worship a bit – a man who is living the rock star life you have only ever, will only ever dream of – somewhere that man is hurting every bit as bad as you, and more. He's feeling every inch of the despair and hopelessness and impotent rage that you are. And he's poured it all out into a wall of sound, and that sound is now in the room with you, and you are not alone.

You can keep 'Everybody Hurts.' *This* is my fucking faith.

Later, I'd learn about some of the horrific biographical problems that lead to the recording of this record. But really, it's all there on the tracks. You don't need a translator.

An album named after the secret track on a record made by a heroin-addict rock star who would later blow his own brains out with a shotgun. Not exactly subtle. Except it *is*, somehow. Its excesses are so violent, so near-total, that it requires an act of endurance to listen past the noise and hear the raw beating heart underneath.

Make that effort, though, focus hard, really fucking *listen* and the rewards are there in spades, and all the sweeter for the trying.

For starters, as dark as it is, it's also hilarious.

Seriously.

Start with the song titles – 'Junkenstein,' 'Nurse

Maximum,' 'Pissjoy.' 'Thunderfuck,' for heaven's sake! And it's not just wry, surface-level gags either, this is a rich vein that runs through the whole record. 'Junkenstein,' for example, starts with levels recorded intentionally too quiet, and then gradually steps up each pattern change, so it's at normal volume by the time you get to the second verse. This means if you're anything like me, you're actually listening to it at a blistering volume, because you turned it up to hear the opening. It's actually kind of a genius way to get you to listen to the record at the volume intended by the artist, but it's also kind of a practical joke too.

'Nurse Maximum' comes off as a love song to Nurse Ratched from *Cuckoo's Nest*. 'Anthem' is a bitter, blistering assault on the notion of the Big Rock Song, but it's also a piss-take of the same, what with the distortion turned up to 15, and **that** chorus. What could top it? Maybe just the gaggle of children delightedly scream-singing the chorus of PissJoy (na na na na na) a couple of tracks later. It's fucking glorious; a reminder of how joyful it is to be a child – and to be swearing.

. The section of 'Soundog Babylon' that drops into a sub-Stone Roses limp groove, before revving back up to that hyper chorus is similarly humorous, in a just-because-we-can kind of way.

And then there's 'Now Is the Colour.'

This is the one where it all comes together for me. Because it's all in here, in the lyric and the pile-driver repeated riff, the teeth-gritting percussion, and the screaming chorus. It's furious, and ugly, and desperate, and bleak, but it's also a joke, a goof, a punchline, each three-line stanza leading to the fourth line punchline payoff of the track's title.

And so on. It's relentless, raging, the energy borne of desperation and fever. It's mesmerising. It's transcendent. It's the clearest illustration I can immediately think of for the gulf between the representation of music as notes on a page and the reality of what a performance can sound like; what it can make you feel. Every time I get to that collapsing end, as the guitar crashes to silence and the sirens wail and the news reporter rattles on incoherently, I'm just left fucking stunned. Every single time.

Just over a year before, Marilyn Manson's seminal *Antichrist Superstar* had been released. I'd initially resisted it, but was eventually won over – inevitably, really. It's intelligent, extraordinary well produced, apparently unhinged noise actually perfectly performed and managed, structurally smart, lyrically dense, and pleasingly nihilistic. It's the soundtrack to the end of the world. Or more accurately, the soundtrack to a slick Hollywood movie about the end of the world. That's not so much a bug as a feature, mind – Manson has always had one eye on the mainstream and his place in pop culture, and he's as much in love with the American culture that he interrogates as he is perplexed by it; as much a product as a producer of product. And *Antichrist Superstar* remains a superb, superlative metal album.

But *Endless, Nameless* shits all over it from a great height.

There are several important reasons why, but in essence they all boil down to the same related factors – authenticity and class.

Because Ginger Wildheart didn't have, or aspire to, a house in the Hollywood hills. He was just an almost supernaturally gifted songwriter with mental health issues that went, as with so many of his peers, untreated and undiagnosed. A man living life at the bleeding edge, not because it was cool or edgy, or to be the next big thing, but because he really had no fucking choice. He was born to work this job, born to make music – anyone who's spent any time with *Earth Vs* can tell you that as a moral certainty. But turns out the music industry in the '90s is actually kind of a desolate and dangerous place for someone gifted but vulnerable – I know, shocker right?

See, Manson's angst and misery is that of a middle-class kid, ultimately. By which I mean, it's the ennui of someone who's had all material needs met but still feels a gaping hole in his life, one that can't be filled by drugs or God or sex. It's music written by someone who is smart enough to know they've won the genetic lottery, being born to the country and class and race that he has, but is also smart enough to realise it's still a crock of shit, and to feel the roaring emptiness at the heart of that existence.

And I say that not to denigrate. That's a real thing – the feeling that you should be grateful, but you're still the ugliest and most awkward kid in the class, the one nobody can relate to, the disconnect and alienation – people get killed over that feeling. To have the courage to put that into words and sound for all us misfits is a good thing.

Similar things are also true of *The Downward Spiral* – another fine, bleak album of the '90s.

But it doesn't touch the sides of the misery and despair of *this* record. *Endless, Nameless* is the sound of a man choking on his own ambitions. It's the sound of a man who's just fallen in love with crack cocaine, knows it is likely to kill him, and cannot stop. It is the sound of a man who has lived the dream only to find it to be a waking nightmare from which there is no escape. It is the sound of that man screaming into the darkness, howling into the void, doing the only thing that makes sense to him, as pained and broken as he is. Doing the one thing he can do, must do; the one thing that even the smack can't quite kill:

Making music. Turning feelings into sounds.

Endless, Nameless is the sound of the abyss. No more, no less. It's not for everyone. It's ragged and distorted and yeah, in places even broken.

It's also a fucking spectacular album. A work of art.

In a way, I'm glad it's obscure, even hated by many

die-hard fans. It should be. It's hard to listen to, and it does not give a fuck if you like it.

But if this record does speak to you, then sister, brother, I feel you.

I feel you.

PS – If you only listen to one track from the album, make it 'Now Is the Colour.' I can't promise it will change your life, but it's not impossible.

...Music. Some kind of...sound? Reproducible sound? Noise, but...I just can't do it, I can't make it make sense. The way it felt though...

I need to know what music is. More important, I have more dates and a title with which to create a search profile – a fairly precise one. Maybe I can start to get a sense of when brain dumps were invented, because that was *just* like being in someone else's head.

<INPUT ENDS>

<INPUT BEGINS>

Well, fuck me.

Spent half the morning poking around in my new 'Red Pill' portal. *Endless, Nameless* existed – came out right when the DNA output said it did. This is significant. If that was the 'year' 1997, and that fact was recorded in a contemporaneous brain dump...the dumper was clearly a young man when the events he's talking about happened.

So how old could he possibly have been when he made the dump? Let's assume he's got perfect recall, somehow; that he can remember back a long way...

<Painful how they flail about, isn't it? Lost in a labyrinth of their own nonsense. Cowering from the Basilisk of their own fevered imaginings. It helps if you can see the funny side, I've found. Anyway, back to the fuck up in progress.>

Well, at some point we had life expectancy in the hundreds, didn't we? Got that from the earlier machine output. Still, it nails it down to a period – a 'century,' in the old measurements. A block of time in which brain dumps *had* to have come into being. And given that they are the high tide mark of post-war tech, by extension, I must be closing in on dating The War itself...

Anyway. That's not the fucked-up part. The fucked-up part is, I was tracing the references back, trying to actually find an example of music. I found out about a specific file type – mp3 – which we had been told were 'junk' files. When I think about all the terabytes of them that I've deleted...

Only, well, it turns out they aren't deleted at all. They're on the 'Red Pill' mainframe. I found them.

Or at least, I found the area they're stored in. It's another subfolder, huge size. Like, almost-as-big-as-the-mainframe huge.

And it's encrypted.

And the Protocol Officer's username and password wouldn't let me in.

<Well, it's no fun if it's TOO easy.>

So, I can report that 'music' exists but I can't get to it, and they won't let you hear it. I don't know why. I mean, to judge by what we've learned here, I guess it does sound kind of dangerous, maybe. But it's also...well, it also sounds powerful.

Maybe those mean the same thing to The Ministry.

Because if we're not *really* trying to recapture history and restore it, but instead actually trying to repress it, to keep it under wraps...

But then why store it, even securely? Why not simply destroy it all? Why the second and third mainframes, nested and encrypted?

The third folder, the one holding the music files is called 'Rabbit Hole'.

<Too much? I can never tell...>

How deep does this thing go?

Okay. Calm head. Let's see what tonight's sample has in—

December, 1984. I am six years old. Neither of my parents were the kind to turn off their TV's when the news came on, so I'd seen it, and I'd asked the kind of questions kids ask. These are the ones I can remember, with the answers I recall. All, some, one, or less of them may be accurate. They feel right, though.

'Where is that?'

'Africa.'

'Why are those people brown?' I grew up in the rural north, then the rural southwest. Outside of TV and very occasional trips to London to visit my Nan, I didn't see black people. At all. They were outside of my realm of experience. I remember feeling no fear or anger or discomfort – only curiosity, and maybe a little caution.

'Because it's very hot in Africa, the sun is very hot, so their skin is brown to stop them getting sunburnt.'

It's Christmas time
There's no need to be afraid

'Why are there so many of them?'

'There's a lot of people in Africa. It's a refugee camp.'

'Why are they living in tents?'

'Because they don't have any money. There's been a drought.'

'What's a—'

'It means there's been no rain, so none of their crops have grown.'

At Christmas time
We let in light and we banish shade

I know this one. Maybe from the harvest festival at school.

'So they don't have any food?'

'That's right. No water to drink, either.'

'Why are there so many children?'

'They have big families.'

'Why? If there's no food or water...'

'They didn't know. Anyway, it's traditional over there. To have big families.'

I'm remembering it wrong, guessing too much. Never mind. It feels right.

> *And in our world, of plenty*
> *We can spread a smile of joy*

'Why are they not moving?'

'They're too tired to move.'

'Why are they so thin?'

'Because they're starving.'

I think about that. About being starving. About long car drives, being late for tea, or waking up early and having to wait for breakfast. Hungry. *Starving.* No; not starving. I look back at the TV. At the stick-thin figures. Really, like a bundle of sticks under brown canvas.

I think I'll never say I'm starving again.

> *Throw your arms around the world*
> *At Christmas time*

'Why do the children have such big bellies?'

'Their bellies are so empty, they've swollen up.'

'Why don't they do anything about all the flies? Brush them away?'

'They don't have enough energy. They're dying.'

Dying. Because it didn't rain and there's no food.

> *But say a prayer*
> *Pray for the other ones*

I knew about praying, at 6. And at 6, I was probably still young enough to do it, at least at school, not having yet noticed the disconnect between what my teachers taught me and what my parents lived. But the thing that really got me was – food. I was surrounded by it. There were whole trays of it every lunch at school, bowls and plates every breakfast and dinner. Our cupboards were *full* of food. So were the shops.

'Why can't we send them our food? We have loads!'

Somewhere in the back of my mind, there's something about a grain mountain, from the news. Surely...

'It's complicated.'

> *At Christmas time, it's hard*
> *But, when you're having fun*

It didn't sound complicated. It sounded simple. Hungry people. Spare food. Heck, it sounded *dumb.*

I think maybe my mother's answer was clearer, albeit bleaker.

'I don't know, son.'

> *There's a world outside your window*
> *And it's a world of dread and fear*

I knew about dread and fear, of course. Up north, the local news had shown people fighting with police, huge crowds of each, something about mines. I'd seen men with guns, and bombs exploding, and plane crashes. There were murderers in the world who got caught – arrested. But they'd killed first. Sometimes children. 'Stranger danger.' There were germs. Diseases. And later...well, later there'd be Challenger and Dunblane and Columbine and 9/11.

But none of that seemed *this* stupid. This...pointless. This solvable. A mountain of food. A continent of starving people.

I didn't get it.

I still don't, truth be told.

Where the only water flowing
Is the bitter sting of tears

It's not complicated. We had food. We had planes. They were children. I knew, instinctively, without having to be told, that this was wrong. It was...an offence. Against morality. Against the notion of humanity. I didn't have the words, but I knew this, felt it deeply. It made me cry when I thought about it. This wasn't how the world was supposed to work. This was **unfair**. And when the song came out, and that closing coda/round kicked in

Feed the world
Let them know it's Christmas time

with crappy synth bells and all, it would bring a lump to my throat, and I'd see those children, my age and younger, with flies in their face and no energy to move them, and I'd think *dying,* and I'd think *starving to death,* and I'd be crying; unable to understand why the singers in the video were smiling, why they weren't crying just thinking about it; how it was that life went on and we all went back to schools and work and reading and TV and eating and drinking and presents and Santa and these children couldn't move and were dying because they had no water and no food. I'd be choked up with useless tears, like I am now.

And please don't give me 'teach a man to fish.' I mean, yes, obviously. Trivially. But fundamentally, feed the fucking starving children, okay? And when they're all fed, with access to safe, clean water and roofs over their heads and clothes on their backs, by all means follow up with a hundredweight of rods and reels and 7 million copies of *Fly Fishing* by J.R. Hartley translated into Ethiopian.

And the Christmas bells that ring there
Are the clanging chimes of doom

And of course, hearing it now it's embarrassing for at least two reasons I can immediately think of, starting with white-person guilt, land-of-not-just-plenty-but-excess guilt, and over-generalising bullshit. Do you have any idea how big Africa is? How diverse? (*Ed: Well, probably **you** do, because you're clearly the kind of educated, sensible person that only reads the finest books. But in a general sense…*) No snow in Africa? Really? Not even on the mountains? The Christian population doesn't know it's Christmas? Ever heard of the **rain** forest? Clue's in the fucking name. No; it's shameful, it is – it's the worst kind of well-meaning yet paternalistic, over-sentimentalised, over-simplified sop to emotion whose sole purpose is to emotionally blackmail your cash out of your wallet and into the charity tin. The chuggers outside Sainsbury's have more integrity, and more dignity. It's fucking shameless, and crass, and gross.

Also…life does go on. We absorb these human and inhumane horrors through our eyes and ears, we take in the fact of child misery and starvation and death, and we feel bad, and say things like 'fucking hell' and 'it's just horrible,' and we *do*, we feel bad, maybe hug our own kids a little tighter come bedtime, or text 'FOOD' or 'WATER' to the number that flashes on-screen, or both. Then, somehow, we go to bed and go to sleep and get up and go to work and max out our credit cards on plastic landfill for kids who'd rather have the cardboard box to play with half the time, and because the starving dying children aren't in our faces *right that very second*, we…forget, and we live in not just comfort but a level of extreme excess.

Like it's not even happening.

And when I say we, I mean first-and-foremost me, just

to be clear. Of sinners, I am the chief. I'll sometimes feel miserable for a whole 15 minutes before turning on *Breaking Bad* or *Justified* or *Hannibal*, and any sleepless nights I suffer from these days don't have much to do with any of this stuff. And for all that I'm giving Geldof and Bono et al. shit here for crimes against song-writing, they have in an immediate and material way done far more to help these people that I will in 100 lifetimes. I speak not so much from the moral high ground as from a deep and muddy ditch.

I don't do anything useful.

And somehow, we've convinced ourselves this is healthy, even normal – that the weird people are the over-sensitive souls who get so upset they can't function thinking about it, who become miserable and depressed and even sometimes suicidal because the obscene imbalance is too much, the naked greed alongside the desperate need just too overwhelming for the conscience to take, when it's displayed so starkly. They're the ones who need medicating. We're normal, because we can just make ourselves indifferent to suffering, as long as we don't have to look at it or think about why it's happening.

I know all that now.

But I was six years old. And to a six-year-old, the song spoke perfectly to the feeling of what was going on. The futility. The awful juxtaposition of my life and the life of those children.

The horror.

And right smack in the middle, the line so dark, and true, and problematic, that they cut it from the latest release, even though Ebola should be far scarier, from a cynical point of view – after all, it's not like starvation is contagious. If ever a dark and unworthy prayer was needed, it's in the face of a disease like this.

But even Bono has lost his stomach for this one, it seems. Which I think is a great pity.

Because sometimes even the crassest and most emotionally manipulative disposable pop art can speak to a deeper, darker truth; can ring true with a statement that shames us with its honesty, it's raw and inherent hypocrisy, and which is really the only sentiment that's come close to explaining all that 'it's complicated' bullshit masquerading as an answer, while the butter mountain melted and the grain mountain rotted and the people of Ethiopia faced mass extinction for lack of clean water and food; a statement that reveals far more than it intends, and little of it to our collective credit, but is undeniably genuine:

Well tonight thank God it's them
Instead of you

...All right. Well...I knew things weren't perfect...and I guess I'm torn between the horror of what is being talked about and the compassion and the expressed desire to reach out, to somehow fix things. But *holy shit*. It's an uncomfortable tension.

And now I've got a concrete date, and an age – six years old. So we had brain dump tech within living memory of 1984. Also some other events to hopefully verify – Challenger, Dunblane, Columbine, 9/11. Wonder what they are?

<You could sure help him out, couldn't you? Would you, I wonder? How comfortable does this sleeping dog look, to you? How blissful is his ignorance?>

These old dumps were clearly a little crude. I'm wondering if there were transposition issues with early models, maybe. It would explain the commonality in language so far – almost as if the capture device had a limited vocabulary to render the thoughts in.

<Painfully so, I'd have said ;) >

Also interesting that it seems to have been used for recording memories of past events rather than in a diary format like we do now. Issues with data storage? Scarcity? Maybe it was costly in terms of resource usage, so people only used it to record striking memories? That would explain the odd way they're so...backwards looking. Or is it just that the machine can only read the most vivid memories?

Still, at least I have something new to fact-check at the office tomorrow.

<INPUT ENDS>

<INPUT BEGINS>

My Protocol Officer was killed today.

Or last night, I guess. 'Data mishandling' was the charge on the bulletin. Execution was carried out immediately upon the crime coming to light.

It's got to be linked to my attempt to use her password to access 'Rabbit Hole,' *which means that they're willing to kill to protect whatever is in that third mainframe.*

And also, my digging around got someone killed. Shit.

I don't know what to do now. Genuinely do not. I couldn't verify the rest of yesterday's data. Didn't dare. Can only access the 'Red Pill' folder with her username. Feels too risky to do that now. Too dangerous.

All that data I've been collecting, collating, the timeline I'd begun to construct; all lost. At least for now. No way to reach out to whoever the 'friend' was that sent me the details in the first place. Can't imagine that they're going to want to help again after this.

I'm feeling badly shook up. I didn't like her particularly, but she got killed over something I did. She knew more than I did. She knew more about what the Ministry is really doing. She's— fuck. I don't have the language for it.

Anyway, whatever she is, was— that's it, isn't it? She no longer is. She *was*. That's on me.

Going to run another sample. Fuck it, I need to—

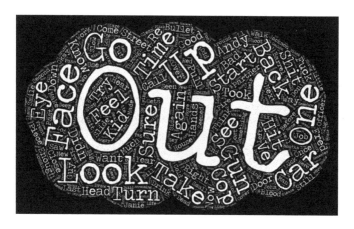

I'm not much of a writer. I know you're gonna think I'm crazy. I'm OK with that. This is the truth. Believe what you want, I'm past caring. I just want to lay it all out, once and for all.

Started at a gun show. My rookie year, '96. I was looking for a piece for Janie. Things were getting serious. I wanted something she could carry for protection. She was an army brat; didn't take much persuading.

I was browsing a trinket stall. Looking for something that would wind up my dipshit liberal brother. Bumper sticker, T-Shirt, 'cold dead hands'; something like that. I remember I was deep in it, so when the guy said 'Can I help you, officer?' it made me jump.

I turned around. Took him in. He was 5' 7", had short, spiked red hair, freckles, clean shaven, 'cold dead hands' T (there it is, I thought), combat pants. Dog tags. (Novelty ones that read 'Yeah, I was in the shit.') Slim build. Classic chickenhawk/rooster type. He spread his hands at hip height, but he was smiling, pleased with himself.

'Hey, sorry, no offence meant. But you are a cop, right?'

I considered not answering, or lying. But what the fuck. Might as well get used to it. 'No. But I'm gonna be. I graduate next week.'

'Hey, congratulations, officer!' His handshake was solid, dry, brief. 'Thank you for your service.'

'Sure.'

Wasn't the first time I'd heard it and it sure wouldn't be the last. There was a period after 9/11 when it was all anyone could say, seemed like. But it was new enough then to still feel awkward.

'Hey, we've got a twenty percent discount for cops and soldiers. Ambulance workers too, but we don't get as many of those.' Shrug. 'What you in the market for?'

'Just browsing.' Polite. Keeping my distance.

I remember how he looked at me then. Staring. Like he was trying to make his mind up about something. I didn't like it.

'How about a good luck charm? I know, I know...' - reading my face - '...sounds hokey. Hell, it is hokey, but still. Who couldn't use a little luck now and again? Especially in this town, am I right?' He flashed a big grin. So sincere and goofy I couldn't help but smile back.

'Sure.'

'Sure! Great! Okay, here we go then...' There was a drawer underneath the table. As he pulled it out, I saw rows and rows of small plastic boxes piled deep. Hundreds, looked like. He ran his finger across them. Glancing up at my face then back down. Frowning. Concentrating.

It felt odd, uncomfortable, but I figured he was driving at something and I was curious. His eyes flicked up again, three times, four, then 'Okay, try this one!'

He held the box up to me. Inviting me to take it. I took it up to eye level. There was a fine silver chain, looped through a small glass or plastic cylinder. Inside that, a single bullet. Looked like a big one: a .44 or .45. Looking close, I could see scratches across the surface of the slug.

'Here.'

He handed me a jeweller's magnifying glass. Smiling again, but a little nervous. Like a con-man feeling his mark swaying in the breeze. I didn't like it, but I took it anyway and looked. Somehow I knew what I was going to see. Sure enough, engraved across the surface of the slug is the word 'John.'

The feeling of knowing, then seeing, made me start. He laughed, clapping his hands together once. Sharp and loud. 'Yes! I guessed right, didn't I?'

Really pleased with himself. I saw no sense in denying it.

'Neat trick. How did you do it?'

He shrugged again, all aw-shucks.

'Dunno, honestly. I get it wrong as often as right. But, shit, I dunno, you look like a John.' He shrugged again. Apologetic.

'Well, what do you think? A bullet, with your name on? Better you have it than someone else, right?'

He smiled again. Again I feel my own face respond. He's harmless, after all.

'How much?'

'Tell you what, just pull a bill out your wallet blind, and I'll take it.'

I think about it. The biggest bill I have is a $20, and...'Sure? I know I've got some singles in there.'

'What can I say? I feel like gambling. Must be in the air. Come on, take it as an apology for spooking you earlier. My bad.'

Sincere, suddenly.

I pulled out a bill blind and handed it over, not looking. He laughed. 'Lincoln, huh?' He shook his head, still grinning. 'That'll teach me! Shit, could have been worse. Here you go, sir.'

He handed me over the box.

'Don't go losing it, now!' he said. Salesman smile sliding back into place.

I graduated as advertised. Married Janie in the fall. Got started in LVPD. Partnered up. Foot patrol. Car patrol. Drunks and whores and pimps and pushers. Vegas was going for the 'family destination' dollar again. We had plenty to keep us busy, trying to keep all that shit off the strip where it liked to be, back down in the ghettos where it belonged. Lots of busts. The odd broken head. Beers with the boys of an evening. The odd double-date with the other married guys. Janie on the pill, not in any hurry to start in on the kids thing.

Good times.

The bullet just sat in my wallet. Forgotten.

Most cops are superstitious, at least a little. Something about having your ass on the line every day. I saw a few St. Christophers, St. Michaels. Stuff like that. One guy had a poker chip from The Stardust. He claimed it had been in Lefty Rosenthal's pocket the day he survived that car bombing.

Not everyone had a good luck charm, but most did.

Anyway.

Andy was my partner. A good kid. Pretty much a straight arrow. I knew that some of the others would sometimes catch a free blowjob from the whores. A bribe for not busting them. Later, when things started going bad, I took a few myself. But not Andy. I can't say that no one deserves what happened to him – I've seen too much evil shit to think that – but he sure didn't.

It was late fall. The overnight shift. Car patrol on the strip. Call comes in.

Officer down.

It's close, ninety seconds out. We hit the blues. Andy floors it. I call it in.

I don't know the guy who's been shot. We're a big force, I've only been on the job eighteen months. Control says he's been responding to a call. Routine DMV. He's hit the red button. No voice contact since. No other info except the last known. I feel sick. Scared. Angry. Stomach like lead. My hands are steady enough as I unclip the holster of my sidearm. The street is lined with small single-storey houses. Old cars out front. Battered plastic kids' toys out on the lawns.

Shitty neighbourhood.

The officer is lying in the middle of the street. On his back. Andy slams on the breaks. Tires screaming. ABS making the car shudder. I have time to see the blood pool under his body. Uniform gleaming with it. It looks bad.

We slide to a halt about ten feet away. One look. No words. We draw and get out of the car as one. Covering the houses that line the street. We walk sideways, backs to each other. Moving towards the cop. Looking for signs of movement.

'Anything?' Glad to hear my voice sounding calm. My heart beating about one-twenty.

'Nope. Wait—'

I start to turn my head in his direction. That's when it

happens. Explosion of sound from my side of the street. The flat crack of rifle fire. Semi-automatic.

My mind freezes. The training takes over. I hit the deck. My peripheral vision picks out Andy doing the same. I bring my gun up. My head turns back to my side of the street.

Time is running slooooow. I can hear each repeat of the rifle. Feel the breeze as a slug passes by my left cheek.

Some nights I wake up feeling that. Sweaty and scared.

Anyway.

I think that I need to get to cover. That we are sitting ducks. Then I see the muzzle flash from the ground-floor window opposite. Instinct takes over.

I fired all fourteen rounds into the side of the house. Ballistics confirmed after I'd hit the perp in six places, including the fatal headshot. At the time, all I knew was that the asshole had stopped shooting. I turned back to the other officer. Saw with no real surprise that he wasn't moving or breathing.

Andy was. He was also drooling blood and looked in a bad way. I dragged him into cover behind our car. Better safe than sorry. Waited for the cavalry.

The CSI boys were pretty surprised afterwards that the shooter had managed to miss me and hit Andy. They took a good look at the angle of the shooter. His field of vision relative to the two of us. Pretty easy to recreate, with the blood pools in the street, my spent casings, what have you. There was a fair bit of head-scratching all round.

'You musta hit the deck quicker, that's all.' It was bullshit. I went along with it. No sense doing otherwise. I thought I just got lucky.

Andy, not so much. He arrested twice, once in the ambulance, once at the hospital. He went under for ten minutes the second time. He didn't come all the way back. Oxygen deprivation. Permanent brain damage. He ended up somewhere near functional, but lost all his speech memory. Had to learn to talk again from scratch. Lost some higher function too. Shitty business.

I'd always been a drinker. Most cops are. I started drinking for real not long after that. To start with, it was just to help me sleep. I kept waking up screaming. Feeling the breeze of a bullet passing my cheek. Again and again. Janie soon had me sleeping on the sofa most of the time. I was waking her up and freaking her out. Of course, that just made me drink more.

I managed to hide it from work: the drinking, the dreams, all of it. PTSD does not look good on a cop's resume, however PC the department was pretending to be. I went to the mandatory counselling, all that crap. I kept my shit together and to myself. Scored a clean bill of health.

TV makes you think that a cop's life is nothing but crazed villains and shoot-outs. That's bullshit. It's mainly boring. Hard, mindless work, with occasional flashes of excitement. It was another five years before someone took a shot at me.

My next partner was Fred. Fred was a real piece of shit. Lazy. Dumb. Fucking gross personal habits. He'd belch loudly every time he ate, laugh like it was funny. He could pick his nose for *hours*, seemed like. Rooting around in there like he was digging for gold. He wasn't a trophy hunter; he ate what he caught. He also had an appetite like a fucking hog and the smallest bladder of any man I've ever known. Which meant that we'd end up stopping once an hour at the nearest food joint, so he could go for a piss and buy more junk on the way out to fill his face with. Goddam car stank of stale food all the time. Made me want to puke.

That's how come we're outside the Double-D downtown that afternoon: him and his small bladder and his fat gut.

It happens fast. One second, we're standing next to the

car in the lot, arguing about the relative merits of custard versus jelly. The next, his face just fucking explodes, rips apart, shredded. Splashes my own face with blood. A swarm of angry bees buzz past my face. The boom of the shotgun blast echoes off the building behind me.

We stand there for a second, frozen. I see Fred try to swallow. The pellets have shredded his face so badly that I can see his tongue working against his teeth through the ragged hole in his cheek.

Then we both drop; me into cover behind a car, him into a bleeding heap. I hit the panic button. *Officer down*. Draw my gun, but the black SUV has already pulled away. In the movies the cop would shoot through the traffic. Somehow manage to only hit the bad guy's car. I just get his plates and call it in.

Turned out to be stolen. Local bangers had just brought in a new initiation test for the youngbloods. Tag a cop, earn your colours. That gang didn't last the year, but the attack on me and my partner turned out to be the first shot of a bloody and nervy summer.

Not for Fred though. For him, the war was definitely over. No brain damage, but he lost an eye. All the plastic in the world, not to mention four months in hospital, couldn't put his face back together. He lost some speech too. Nerve damage to his jaw. Talked like he had a mouth full of cotton balls.

He took a medical discharge and pension. Six months after, on the first anniversary of the shooting, he finished the job with his own .45.

What happened before, to Andy, had messed me up. It was a walk in the park next to Fred. Not because of him – piece of shit. No. Just because...

I'd seen the gun fire out of the corner of my eye. Seen the fire spitting out of the barrel. The eyes of a dragon coming to life. I'd known for sure that I was dead. My partner's face disintegrated and what seemed like a thousand pellets buzzed past my face, close enough to feel. To hear. Parting in front of my nose like Moses and the red sea.

The drinking got heavier. My marriage collapsed. She walked one evening while I was on shift. Left a Dear John. Sweet, really. Still caring. We had barely spoken in months. I could hardly remember her face, seemed like. Except, no, that's not right. I can picture her now, if I close my eyes. It's more like the face of a stranger though. Not connected to anything.

Anyhow. By then there was only the bottle and the job. And the job was starting to turn to shit.

Cop humour is legendarily black. What you may not realise is that it can also be very cruel. With two partners down in six years there were bound to be jokes. It started with a printed note taped to my locker: 'To lose one partner could be seen as bad luck. To lose two starts to look like carelessness.'

I left it on there, to show I could take the joke. It ate at me. The other cops started to pull away too. Distance themselves. Offers to go out after a shift for beers or a meal seemed strained, insincere. They stopped asking long before the excuses turned stale. That was okay. By then I preferred drinking alone. Sometimes, when I was lying on my couch, trying to get drunk enough to sleep, I'd take the bullet out of my wallet and hold it up to the light. Look at it. Usually I'd pass out…eventually. Every time I woke up, my fist would be closed around it. Holding it close.

Got through a lot of partners. The usual way. No one wanted to work with me for long; a combination of my rep and my increasing distance. It was fine by me. I had no ambition beyond serving my twenty and getting my pension. I had a vague idea that if I could somehow do that, I could maybe get clean. Get a little bit of my life back. Drunk logic.

A DV call in '09 puts paid to that. Jackson and me are the first responders. Neighbours report yelling. Breaking glass. Kids crying. In the two minutes it takes us to make the address, dispatch gives us an ex-husband and restraining order linked to the residence. A sheet long enough for us to realise whatever is going on tonight has probably been coming for a while.

None of this is new to me by this time, but my gut is tighter than normal. Because, kids.

'Okay. I say we've got P.C., so we go in heavy. You take the back, try and get the woman and the kids out, if you can. I'll take the front, try and nail the suspect. Questions?'

'None.' Jackson already has his piece drawn. Ready for a quick exit.

'Good. Kids're more likely to be at the rear, but stay sharp. If the perp is armed, he gets one warning – after that, he fails to comply in any fucking way, put him down. Do not try to be a hero. Got it?'

I flick my eyes from the road to Jackson's face for a second. He meets my gaze level. Nods quickly. He's got kids. I know he won't fuck about.

'Okay, let's do it.'

I pull the car up outside the house, across the street. Kill the engine. The lights are on. There's yelling. Screaming. Crying.

'I'm giving you sixty, then I'm taking the door.'

Jackson doesn't reply. Dives out the door and runs across the street, low. Heading for the side alley.

I wait in the car for a slow thirty. Get out and walk across the street, up to the front door. Gun drawn and pointing at the ground. Heart beating slow but heavy.

I can hear kids crying. A woman screaming. My gut turns cold as I reach the door. The screen door is unlocked. Opens quietly. The door itself looks cheap. Like the house, the neighbourhood. Good. I draw a last breath, deep. Brace. Gun up now.

My kick splinters the thin wood around the lock. The door flies inward, banging off the interior wall, swinging back.

'Police!'

I take in the scene down the sight of my pistol. An open living room/dining room. A woman standing by the dining table, sobbing. Hysterical. In a T-shirt and panties. Clinging to each leg, terrified, snot faced rugrats stare bug eyed at me.

No, past me.

My blood runs cold. Things go very slow. I hear the click as my head turns. The sliding sound of a semi-automatic pistol being cocked. My own gun pointing the wrong fucking way. My head snapping round. Upper body turning as well. Too slow. Too little. Too late. The gun floats into focus. A big one, Glock or Desert Eagle. The barrel like a huge, black, sightless eye.

I look up the sights. Right into the eye of a terrified, angry, desperate man. His finger already adding that last crucial pound-per-square-inch. I want to say no. Please don't. In that moment I want to live so bad. I am too slow and it is too late.

He pulls the trigger.

He is less than ten feet away when the gun pointed right at my head goes off. The noise of the explosion is deafening. I watch the top of the barrel slide back as the bullet fires. I see the flash as the powder ignites. I have time to wonder if I will see the slug leave the barrel before it hits me. The barrel is still sliding, moving backwards. Disengaging from the rest of the gun. Exploding. The eye of my killer doesn't have time to change to surprise before it is obliterated by the lump of hot metal. His head snaps back against the wall. His legs give. He slides down, dead before his ass hits the floor. All I can do is stand there, gun pointed at him, staring – beyond disbelief, beyond shock, in some numb other world, a ghost – as Jackson bursts in yelling questions, checking out the woman and the kids, calling for backup, CSI, ambulance.

They called it shock. Put me in overnight for observation. That was all it took. The pill they gave me got me through the night, but no power on earth could stop the DTs from hitting in the morning. Just like that, I was done.

There was plenty of sympathy. Shrinks. But the word was out, and by then I'd just had enough. I didn't want to get better. I just wanted to drink enough so that I wouldn't see Fred's tongue working his teeth through that hole in his face; the gun exploding in the apartment; Andy lying in a pool of his own blood.

It should have been me. That's the beginning and the end of it. It should have been me. Would have been me. Andy was great and Fred was a jerk and the restraining-order violator was a piece of shit, but none of that matters.

It should have been me.

I know that now. As sure as I know that the end isn't going to be found in the bottom of this bottle.

I'm going to use the .44 I bought for Janie. She left it behind when she walked. It just feels right. Plus I'm sure that the bullet will fit just fine. Feels like it's been waiting for this moment, the years between, just one bad dream.

I'm done dreaming now.

...What am I doing this for? Why am I putting myself through all this...this endless chain of misery? I can't risk trying to verify any of this any more, even with that message that I got sent...

Hang on.
Hang on!

<INPUT ENDS>

<INPUT BEGINS>

Okay, so basically, I'm a total fucking idiot. Sorry, but I am. Also, sorry for all the swearing. *Because I've finally figured out who you are.*

But first, verification – I don't need to do any more. The evidence at this point is (i) overwhelming and (ii) either locked up in Ministry vaults or on the terabytes of storage devices that Field Officers are still pulling out of the ruins of the old cities.

The truth is already out there. The problem is, *you* can't get to it.

But that's okay, because I can. I did. This machine is the key to restoring history for all of you.

Yeah, I'm talking to all of you. Not yet, obviously, but soon. Because someone sent me a message. Straight into my brain, via the brain dump link, without a wire.

Which means these things, these wonderful devices that every citizen is now fitted with at the age of ten, are capable of receiving data remotely.

By broadcast.

All I have to do is figure out how to send messages. The way my 'friend' did.

<I knew he's get there sooner or later. Actually, I thought it would have been considerably sooner. Alas.>

A message to all of you. This message. The evidence that the Ministry is *not* working to reclaim our shared past and knowledge, but to repress it.

Sure, they'll kill me. Possibly destroy the machine, too. But I think that won't matter. Because I think that if every single living citizen of age, all seven million of you, get this broadcast at once, there won't be enough Ministry Police in the world to stop you tearing the whole rotten thing down.

It's going to take time to figure it all out, obviously. And I'll need to keep running the samples in the meantime – give you as much to go on as I can when I finally do broadcast.

Also, they'll kill me. So there's that. Sigh.

Fuck it. I need some sleep

<INPUT ENDS>

<INPUT BEGINS>

So today I got made the new Protocol Officer for my area. It was fucking insane. They took me into this windowless room – I'd always thought it was a closet or something, but it's decked out like an interrogation room, I just about shit myself when I walked in - and a very serious man in a suit was sat on the other side of the desk. I came *that close* to running.

I can barely remember the questions now. Delayed shock, I guess. Lots of shit about security, understanding the need for discretion, all of that. I remember feeling like my whole skull was throbbing with my heartbeat – until I realised that the metric analysis they were talking about was my suitability to take on the role.

So there it is. I'm now K-POX, Protocol Officer (Orange Band clearance). Hints were made of further promotions if I do well. No threats were made which, given how the last incumbent left, would have been superfluous I suppose.

Incredible. I had to sign a bunch of stuff, of course. Induction should be amusing, as they explain to me how all this stuff I had been told was unverified is actually restricted, but I'll put in some time practising my straight face tonight and hopefully not get myself killed before I can get back into the 'Red Pill' mainframe. With my own username this time, and therefore my own head on the block, I suppose.

It makes absolutely no sense. I'm stuck between amazement and terror. It's nauseating. I don't understand how it can't be a trap, but I also don't understand how it *can* be. Most of all, I don't understand how any 'algorithm' can possibly have spat out my name. Either it's some kind of elaborate trick or...shit, I don't know, maybe the whole thing's built on nothing but broken programming.

Either way, I've got some digging to do. But that's for tomorrow. They sent me home early 'to prepare.' I've done some light tweaking to the machine settings. If I'm now getting brain dump outputs, hopefully the slight adjustment I've made should start pulling out 'live' dumps, as opposed to these weird reminiscences. So let's see—

For Jason, it was love at first sight.

'Mummy! Ted!'

Snatching him out of the gutter. Holding him up to her. Excited. Enraptured. Caz had seen that look enough times to know what it meant.

She regarded Ted wearily. The 'fur' was a dirty dishcloth grey that made her want to wash her hands just looking at it. His eyes were crude stitches of dark blue thread – vacant X's. The nose was a loosely-threaded button that might well have come from the cardigan of an aged child molester (and was, in Caz's opinion, practically a dictionary illustration of 'choke hazard'). The belly sagged unpleasantly, like the beer gut on a wife-beater. There was the faintest waft of mould. Two arms and two legs and two ears, all the same grubby shade.

There was no polite way to say it: Ted was hideous. Hideous enough that it actually took a little effort for her to turn her gaze to Jason. His little face was excited beyond all reason, eyes shining with the warmth of true love, pure and complete and possessing, that only a toddler can feel.

Ah, crap.

Caz thought about resisting. She thought long and hard, because she really didn't like the look of Ted. At all. But she could visualise with perfect clarity the scene that would unfold if she did – the tears, the tantrum and, worst of all, the incessant screaming. Just the effort of thinking about it wore her out.

Screw it. Let him keep it.

'Ted looks like he needs a wash, don't you think?'

'Ted!'

'Yes, Ted looks dirty! Shall we wash him when we get home?'

With bleach. Or fire for preference.

'Ted! Home!'

'Yes, yes, we'll take Ted home and give him a wash, OK?'

'Ted!'

With the tired and heartfelt sigh that is the universal signal of maternal surrender, Caz took Jason's free hand and continued walking home.

'Ted!'

Jason's face was red now. Angry.

'Ted!'

'Yes, sweetheart, Ted needs to go in the washing machine. He's dirty and Mummy needs to clean him.'

'Ted!'

Eyes narrowed, nostrils flaring, mouth a thin angry slash. *So much like his father in his rage*, Caz thought for the millionth time, hating Jason just a little for the reminder. Hating herself for the reaction. The old, dull, helpless despair came flooding back – as it had so often in the months since Andy cut and ran – threatening to sweep her away, to drown her.

But here was Jason, dragging her back. As he always did. Her sweet, sweet boy.

'Jason, Ted needs a clean, that's all. You can see him, here,' – tapping the glass door of the washing machine – 'he'll be okay. It's like Ted having a bath! It'll be fun for him!'

'No! Ted!'

Clutching the bear tight, hugging him protectively. Caz recognised the futility of what she was trying to do – reason with a two-year-old; might as well try to win an argument with a brick – and she snapped.

'Give me that bloody thing!'

Snatching, grasping hard, tugging. Jason was standing in front of her, arms crossed over Ted's stomach, so she was left grabbing at one of those misshapen, stubby legs.

As her grip tightened, she felt its contents shift and grind together, like sand or pebbles. The texture of his skin was clammy and faintly nauseating. Still, she tightened her grip, meaning to tug him out of her son's grasp.

'NO!'

Hysterical, furious, Jason struck out at his mother's face with all the strength in his two-year-old body. Hard enough to hurt. Hard enough to bring a tear to her eye, and more than hard enough to cause her to drop Ted's leg in shock.

He ran from the room immediately, sobbing but not wailing, still defiant and angry. Caz stayed on her knees, staring at the open doorway, the hand that had clutched Ted's leg now tracing the shape of the blow on her cheek. More tears fell then, and she let them. Kneeling on the kitchen floor, she wept bitter tears of hopelessness and rage, and of frustrated, trapped love. The tears pooled on the cheap linoleum and soaked into her jeans.

The day passed as they do. Jason watched TV, played with his trucks and cars, ate, had his nappy changed. He laughed and cried and belched and farted. The only difference was his new constant companion. Ted stayed by his side, paw crushed into Jason's right hand. Caz recalled the dank feeling of the fur, the weird texture of the stuffing, and she wondered how Jason could stand it. But there it was.

With each new activity she thought Jason would finally need both hands and release Ted, but he did not. It got so she almost suspected that Jason could read her mind, that he knew she wanted to separate them (*only to clean the damn thing, for crying out loud*) and he would not allow it to happen. Then she remembered a simple truth: he was a two-year-old – stubborn as only a two-year-old could be – and the thought relaxed her.

Come bath time, Caz had assumed that Jason would give up Ted easily enough. Not a bit of it.

'No! Ted!'

She saw the look in his eye, felt a tingle on her face where he had struck her before, and immediately decided not to push it. Forget it. Let him take Ted into the bath. Let him take the damn thing to bed if he wanted to. Once he was asleep, she could retrieve the godforsaken thing easily enough and clean him.

Or, you know, get rid of him. It.

'Okay, Jason, okay. But you have to get undressed, okay?'

Jason immediately swapped Ted to his left hand and held his arm out for her to pull the sleeve of his jumper.

Cute.

In this way, she undressed him, Ted swapping from hand to hand, Jason's grip firm, unrelenting. She was sure he'd get dropped in the bath, but no. Jason sat in the tub with one hand out over the edge, dangling Ted above the bathroom floor while his mother washed him. Caz ignored this as best as she could, but she couldn't help stealing glances at Ted, as he swung to and fro. His distended belly. His blank, expressionless face. Twisting.

'Up, please. Mummy!'

'Good boy! Milk time?'

'Milk! Tee-vee!'

Some things don't change, she reflected with a smile. She lifted Jason from the bath and into a radiator-warmed towel.

Jason curled up on the sofa and drank his milk just like always, watching his usual bedtime programme with heavy eyes. He acquiesced willingly enough to his mother putting on his pyjamas and brushing his wet hair, though the dressing followed the same routine as the undressing had, with Ted moving from hand to hand in constant contact. Caz observed this with frustration but no real surprise. It was okay. Jason would be asleep soon enough.

Some things didn't change.

Sure enough, his eyes glazed...went half-lidded...then closed. He continued to work the bottle in his sleep, and Caz watched this very ordinary miracle with the same overwhelming wave of love it always engendered. Jason. Her little man. She gently placed her hand on his chest, feeling his breathing, his heartbeat. Remembering when that heart beat inside her. His jaws slowed and finally stopped working the bottle.

Gone.

She kept her hand there a while longer, enjoying his warmth and the rhythm of his sleeping body. Gradually, her gaze turned to his hand, still gripping the arm of that grotty little bear.

Ted.

He - it - was face down on the sofa, which was a mercy. But even the sight of his mangy fur gave her a frisson of disgust almost strong enough to make her shudder.

Christ, that thing was ugly.

She reached for it, then hesitated, remembering the feel of that skin and its contents. She did not want to touch it again, she realised. Quite powerfully did not, in point of fact. Still, Jason had clearly fixated, so that was that. But at the very least...

'At the very least, you, my furry little friend, are having

a bloody bath.'

Unaware that she'd spoken aloud, she reached for Ted and gripped his midsection. The fur still had a damp and somehow warm feel, like that of a dog with a fever. Worse, as her fingers began to sink into what she found herself thinking of – with rising disgust – as his flesh, she felt again the sensation of near-solid objects moving and grinding beneath her grip. The sensation was exquisitely unpleasant and she wondered how Jason could possibly stand it. Still, she got enough of a hold to *pull*.

Jason's eyes flew open immediately, his free hand tugging the bottle from his mouth. Caz jerked back in surprise and fear, releasing Ted and rocking backward.

'No, Mum. Ted. Bed.'

Not angry this time, *thank God*. Not angry, but firm just the same. Certain. *Cold?* Caz let out her breath with a bark that was not quite a laugh and not quite a sob, but could have been either. Or both.

'Okay, Jason, okay, don't worry. I'm not gonna take him. Bed time?'

'Bed.'

'Okay.'

She carried him up the stairs, heart hammering unpleasantly against her ribs. Jason's anger had been one thing, but this...calm certainty – so outside his usual nature – was something else. Up until that moment, Caz's feelings on the subject of Ted had been merely displeasure and contempt. This moment was the first time she'd felt fear. The taste was bitter.

Well, screw it. Just screw it, that's all. She'd put Jason in the cot, then take the damn thing. He could scream and cry all he wanted – scream the bloody house down – she was taking that bear and he was going in the bloody rubbish bin and that'd be the end of it. That second touch had convinced her, even before her son had woken up to command her in that calm, cold voice. Ted was bad fucking news and Ted was not welcome in her home.

But when they got to Jason's bedroom, her son did something totally unexpected: he gave Ted up as easy as pie. Just as she went to lay him down in the cot, he got his legs under him and stood, holding Ted out to her.

'Ted. Mum.'

'You...you want me to take Ted? Mummy take Ted?'

'Yeh.'

Okay.

She reached into the cot, and Jason released him without a moment's hesitation. The sensation of discomfort at holding the thing was still there, but Caz barely noticed, so powerful was her relief (and deeper, her gratitude) at her son's sudden change.

Jason pointed to the corner of the room.

'Ted.'

Caz sighed. So close...but ah-well, still an improvement. Ted wasn't in the cot, and there'd been no bedtime screaming fit. Most importantly, Jason had given him up. Could she stand to leave him in the room? She was relieved to discover that she could, under the circumstances. Ted could sit in the corner for now and take a late night bath once Jason was asleep. Hell, she could probably have him dry and back in place by the morning. The worst of her boy's possessive fever had apparently broken and all else could be forgiven, negotiated.

'You want Ted to sit in the corner?'

'Yeh.'

'All right.'

She carried him – it – over to the corner of the room, next to the radiator and she sat him there, facing the crib.

'There. Okay?'

'Yeh.'

Sleepy. Lying down.

'Good. Ted still needs a bath though, okay?'

'Yeh.'

'All right, we'll do that tomorrow then, yes?'

'Yeh.'

Half-asleep already. Drifting. She crossed back to the cot.

'I love you Jason. I love you so, so much. Sleep tight, little man. See you in the morning.' She leant in, kissed his forehead, tousled his hair gently, and left the room, turning off the light on her way out.

Her intention was to put Ted through the washing machine that evening, but intentions are poor and fleeting things. The wave of relief at Jason's change of heart carried her to the bottle of wine in the kitchen, then the TV called her to the sofa with the promise of her soap opera, then a movie she really liked. Somewhere around her second glass, she felt the tension of the day evaporate in the warming, numbing glow, and by her fourth glass, she'd forgotten Ted ever existed.

She made her way slowly and a little unsteadily up the stairs, brushed her teeth, then all but fell into bed. Two minutes after her head hit the pillow, she was snoring deeply.

In her dream, Jason was crying. Great, lusty cries of pain and fear. She was in a gigantic house, a mansion full of long corridors. She ran down them, flinging open door after door, running into room after room; all huge, all identical, all empty. His screams seemed to be coming from everywhere and nowhere, and her terror increased with each empty room, until she sprang awake, drenched in sweat and yelling 'Jason!'

Her heart beat fast and hard, her mind still trying to shake the horrible vividness of the dream. Then her brain caught up with the frantic signal from her ears. The crying hadn't stopped – it was, in fact, rising in pitch and volume. *Hysterical. Agonised.*

Muscles locked, screamed, flung her out of bed as if she were on wires, propelling her with such force towards her bedroom door that she collided with it even as her hand dove for the handle.

An incoherent prayer tumbling
 from her lips, unknown and unheard, her hands tore the door open with such force that it rebounded and smacked her hard on the shoulder as she passed through it, though she was oblivious to the injury and the pain. Indifferent to anything but the screams of her son.

She flung open his bedroom door as the screams ended on an impossibly high note – abruptly cut off – and she knew, with a cold finality, that she was too late, even as the prayer continued to babble, and her hand scrabbled like an injured spider for the light switch.

The bulb flashed on, flooding the room with awful, harsh light, obliterating shadow. Ted lay in the corner, now just a curled ball of dead skin. His face gazed at the ceiling and two dark, moving trails led from his crude, lifeless, eyes.

In those last precious seconds of lucidity, her eyes sent her mind images it could not process, leaving her to see without comprehension. The trails were seething, boiling, rippling. As she followed their movement, head turning slowly (too slowly) toward the cot, her gaze began to pick out the individual creatures, crawling over each other; shining black bodies, carapaces like beetles, but leaner, more like ants, tumbling and scrabbling over one another in their eager procession.

The trails parted at the bars of the crib before closing

again, becoming a writhing, roiling black blanket. Her head continued to turn, so slowly, like an automatic action, eyes rolling in their sockets, and somewhere deep down a voice was saying *don't look don't look don't look don't look don't—* But still her head turned, still her eyes refused to close. The dark swarm covered a bulge exactly the size and shape of her infant son. His legs, torso, and chest were all swaddled in the chittering, consuming darkness, shining and simmering like a layer of tar. The understanding lurked, pregnant, on the edge of her consciousness, and still her eyes moved.

Until they came to rest on his face.

There she observed with perfect clarity the bleached white paleness of his skin; his eyes wide, sightless, vacant, *gone; his* mouth thrown open, cheeks stretched taut in a frozen mask of agony and terror. Still screaming that final, soundless cry.

The moment held, unwound. Her last second of conscious thought unspooling, stretching, becoming thin. Eyes and heart and mind pulled past breaking point by that awful, pleading face.

Then the creatures, burrowing from beneath, boiled up out of his mouth and across his face, consuming, devouring with an awful scraping, grinding, cracking noise, like boots marching over gravel, and the shape of his body began to sink, becoming indistinct.

Collapsing.

Comprehension dawned, finally – a thermonuclear wave of total destruction that obliterated her conscious mind with awful, devastating mercy.

Her now-unseeing eyes remained there until the creatures, summoned by her smell and the promise of fresh meat, crawled up and over her face and ate them from their sockets.

Ted fed.

...Gonna puke gonna puke gonna—

<INPUT ENDS>

<INPUT BEGINS>

Sorry. Sorry. Fuck. More Enemy activity, do you think? Is that part of how they attacked us? Fuck! The cruelty, the—
 No way I sleep tonight. No way I run another sample either.

<INPUT ENDS>

<INPUT BEGINS>

You'll need to seize the mainframe. You'll have to. I don't know for sure if they'd be able to destroy it, if they saw you coming...but they might. I think if they can, they will.
 And you know, if they do, not the end of the world – there's so much data out there still, sitting on redundant storage devices. Enough for several lifetimes for all of you. But you'll save so much time if you can grab the mainframe.
 If I can get this message to *you* without alerting *them*, somehow.
 Hmm.
 Induction proper started today. I got my username and password. They are the same ones that belonged to the old Protocol Officer, which gave me a nasty shock. Think I covered okay – they made such a big deal out of it, revealing that encryption exists, that I was one of the

'trusted few' to have this info, selected by algorithmic blah blah blah. I guess they took my start of recognition as, I dunno, pride or something.

<'Algorithmic blah blah blah'. I swear, you fucking people.>

Lying, by the way. That's what they call it. Not 'playing,' apparently. 'Lies.' They were very serious about this. Sombre about what an honour it was to have become a 'liar.'

I guess my disgust looked like awe.

Anyway, my official job is twofold now: (i) make sure the team is uploading roughly the expected amount of unverified data per week, and (ii) keep an eye on the 'restricted area' dashboard. If anyone on the team happens to come across an encrypted file and attempts to open it ('like you did,' the trainer said at that point, and I really didn't like his grin) pull them in immediately, assess them carefully, and make a full report.

That's it. Other than that, my time is my own. For this I get a one-third wage increase, access to the Officer's Lounge, and the threat of execution if I don't discharge my duties.

Considering I have no options, things could be worse.

I really can't figure out how this has happened. They keep going on about 'selection by analytics,' which can only mean the system is far more broken than anyone realises. Either that, or everyone else on the team is even worse at their jobs than I was. Do you suppose my evasions when I was being questioned about the opening of the restricted file was part of it? Showed that I had potential, might adapt well to lying?

Or did my mysterious 'friend' rig things somehow? How does any of this really work?

In other news, 'Red Pill' is on my new password-protected terminal. So there's that.

So. I guess tomorrow it's time to sniff around brain dump tech information. Try and figure out how to get this message out to you.

Wish me luck. And in the meantime—

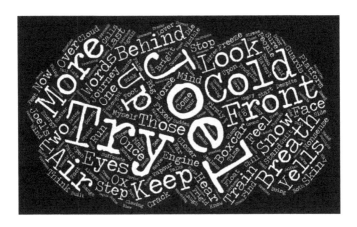

'You have to let me do this.' Joel doesn't look up, and I don't look over. His words float over to me on a cloud of vapour, his breath visible in the frigid air.

'You can't,' I say, eyes fixed firmly on the snow in front of me, trudging up the platform. '*I can't*. I haven't the energy.'

'Sure you do! You're an ox!'

I laugh, despite myself. Joel always calls me that. Once upon a time, I was a big man. Now my skin hangs off me, the chill wind clawing at the skin of my face like a jealous lover.

It is so bright, the cold sunlight bouncing off the bright snow, hurting my eyes. I squint and keep marching. One foot in front of the other.

Joel speaks again. 'You have to let me. It's my fault.'

'Don't start that nonsense,' I say, angry but also scared.

Joel's guilt is a physical thing, eating at him far worse than the starvation has.

'It's not nonsense. We're doing this, brother.' As he talks, we approach the front carriage of the train. The boxcar door stands open, the gloom inside promising false shelter.

I think about the stream of people behind me, and the conditions of the last journey. *Those on the outside will freeze, and those in the middle will suffocate.*

I can't know it, but as soon as the thought enters my mind it solidifies into fact.

I risk a glance up. There are two guards with rifles in front of the engine. Only two. More behind of course, many more, but maybe...

'I'll distract them both. You just run. Once you're on the other side of the engine, cross the tracks and head for the trees.'

We're only half a dozen steps now from the boxcar entrance. I try and formulate a sentence, try to find the words that will stop Joel's madness, but as I look into the darkness of the boxcar, the words freeze in my mind. All I can think about is the last journey, the journey to come, the destination...

I'd rather die here. On my feet.

It's a selfish thought, but also a freeing one. And I realise too that this is what Joel wants, what he was built for, perhaps: his need to be the saviour, the martyr – his compulsion to try to save people.

I try to find a way to say this, or some of it. Too late. We've taken three more steps, then four, and then Joel yells and hurls himself at the two guards.

The sudden movement and noise floods my system with adrenaline; tired, wary muscles coming to life, and I launch into a dead sprint.

I keep my eyes focused on the platform, on the front of the train. Every step takes me closer. My breathing is already ragged. I can hear yelling and the sounds of struggle to my right as Joel makes his stand. Worse, I hear shouts from behind. Harsh barks yelling at me to stop.

I do not stop. I keep running, feeling my blood sing, my throat burn with the cold air. I see the front of the train engine drawing closer.

I feel a blow in my back, and hear a sharp crack. It knocks the air from me, and I stumble. I try to regain my balance, try to breathe in, but I can't.

I fall forwards onto my face.

The powdery snow embraces me. I keep trying to breathe, but I cannot. The shock of the cold causes me to go rigid. Behind me, there are more yells, more of those dull cracks. Some screams.

I feel the cold spread throughout my frame. Filling me. Claiming me.

Carrying me away.

...What was that? Guards? The Enemy? Is this a dispatch from The War? How does it tie in with Ted?

Am I closing in on the source, perhaps?

Fuck it. I'm going to run another sample. I'll be dead on my feet tomorrow, but—

The mist swirls around me. No, fog. It's thick, chilly. It clings to my coat, leaving beads of moisture like tiny glistening eggs on the woolly fibres.

It's dark. The world is grey and I can't make out a light source, but I can see a short distance ahead and behind. It's like being inside of a ten-foot dome. Beyond, that grey wall of gently-writhing water vapour.

My hands ache with the cold. I push them deep into my jacket pockets, hunching my shoulders. The air is thick enough that each inhalation feels damp as well as chilling, cold enough that I see my breath join with the mist on each exhale.

I'm moving forward. I feel the cold through my trousers, but oddly the damp cloth doesn't seem to chill my skin.

I'm headed somewhere. There's a definite directional pull. My mind pulls up an image of a needle in a compass, swinging back to north.

I keep walking. I'll know it when I see it.

The ground is even but not slippery, despite the moisture in the air. My boots grip with ease. My toes are warm inside fluffy socks.

I can't remember how I got here. I walk and try to think, but the swirling nature of the fog keeps throwing up half-shapes and figures to distract me, and my curiosity keeps trying to pivot to where, exactly, the light is coming from; how it can be all about with no clear source. Maybe it's not an external source. Maybe the fog...

Then I hear a sound from up ahead. It's a tapping, knocking sound. Wood on wood. My temperature doesn't change, but I shiver just the same. It's a heavy sound, pregnant even. *What foul beast,* I half think, and shudder again. But there's no doubt – the noise is dead ahead.

My destination.

I feel foreboding bloom in my chest, spreading throughout my body, like there's a lump of ice in my heart suddenly, pumping a numbing dread through my whole system.

My feet keep moving. My boots rise and fall. The quality of my footsteps changes. The sound of each footfall becomes hollow, echoey, and underneath that, I begin to become aware of an organic, slapping sound. My mind conjures an image of damp corpse hands, clapping together in some arrhythmic applause. My scalp prickles. I smell decay, brine, and just as I picture the hands rising, perhaps gripping my ankle to pull me into the ground, my mind makes the connection between sound and smell: I'm on a pier.

It helps, a bit. The corpse hands become the waves they always were, lapping against the supports of the platform I must be on – as if on cue, the wood creaks beneath my feet – but the water is cold and black and very deep, poisoned with salt. In my mind I see tentacles, bone-white and massive, pushing up from the deep (razor sharp suckers designed to rend flesh, sharp enough to cut bone and strong enough to suck marrow), rising towards the hated dim glow overhead; the rickety structure that sticks out like a crude finger over the realm of...

There's a light ahead. It's a flame, I think. There's an orange tinge to it, and it flickers and dances. It's directly in front of me. In my way. I know beyond doubt that this flame is what is pulling me forwards. Part of me is comforted. After all, it's a real light as opposed to this amorphous glow I'm currently surrounded by. Flame offers the chance of heat, and company.

Of course under the circumstances, company is pretty well the definition of a double-edged sword. I move forward anyway, legs on automatic. The wood beneath me creaks more often, and the waves sound closer – surely an illusion, some kind of auditory mirage? The light grows, resolving to a single bright flame. I find it hard to credit that anything could burn so bright in this air, but the fire stands tall in defiance of the atmosphere. It appears to create a halo of clear air around it, burning the fog away.

The flame is flickering some seven feet above the ground. As I draw closer, the glow it casts illuminates the wooden floor. Rough planking, warped with age, rickety. The platform is perhaps ten feet wide. Beyond that, perfect darkness and the aroma of salt.

Beneath the flame, a figure appears, emerging as though being birthed from the fog itself, or perhaps formed *of* it. He is tall, over six foot, and in his right fist he holds the flaming torch aloft. The light is bright yellow and billows around the lumpen end of the handle, like some out-sized juggling prop. The smoke is thick and black, rising a few feet before being absorbed by the grey air.

The hand that grips the handle is large and gnarled. The flame flickers and rolls, strobing over his pale, grubby knuckles. The arm that raises the fist is scrawny but thick. Muscles show under dirty, leathery skin. My gaze moves to his bare shoulder, rounded and powerful. His robe is made of a coarse dark cloth, held at the waist with a thick rope belt. The hood is down, lying crumpled around his neck.

My feet carry me inexorably forward as his face swims

into focus. His features are aged, weathered, but his eyes are still vital, almost wild. They stare aggressively from underneath dark-grey brows, bushy and tangled. His forehead is very high, but long messy braids of black hair lie about his neck, spilling either side of his face. His nose is large and misshapen, as if by injury or disease. His mouth is set in a frown, above an imposing, jutting chin.

My boots step towards him with an inexorable, unbroken rhythm. As I take him in, I feel a resonance within. I still understand very little about where I am, or why, but I suddenly intuit much. It's a deeply unsettling feeling.

I stop, roughly ten feet from the figure. Rather, my legs stop moving. We regard each other.

'You know who I am.' His voice is deep and cracked and resonant.

'Actually, I...'

'You know who I am.' It's not a question, I realise. With dismay, I also realise the truth of the statement.

'Yes.'

He nods. The torch moves from one hand to the other, and he holds it out over the edge of the pier. The yellow flame ripples, bathing a crude wooden rowing boat with flickering light.

'You will cross with me. Soon.'

I nod, feeling my eyes itching, my throat contracting. I'm scared. I'm also sad.

'But first...'

He lowers the torch, igniting an iron brazier filled with logs (which I could almost swear wasn't there a moment ago). The twisted, dry wood almost explodes into flame. I flinch, and the heat is uncomfortable on my exposed face, almost painful, but I do not move back.

'...first, you face your enemies.'

I feel sweaty, and the sudden flame is only part of the reason. My stomach tightens.

'You have questions.'

'I— yes.'

'I will allow you to ask three.'

'Why is it always three?' It's out before I can stop it. But honestly, I've always wanted to know.

'Because it always is.'

His face doesn't change, but I swear that I see something flicker in his eyes – some cold amusement, or contempt. He holds up his free hand, palm out, little finger held under his thumb. Then he lowers his ring finger also.

Two left.

I curse myself. My mind swirls. So many questions...but it seems like there's only one that really matters.

'I have to fight my enemies now?'

'No.'

'Then what?'

'You have to decide.'

'Decide what?'

He is silent. His eyes look to his now closed fist, then back to my face.

No more questions.

He gestures at the brazier. The flame roars higher, and as it dies down, a figure steps out from behind it. It's a boy, an infant. Dark bowl haircut, a T-shirt and jeans. He's handsome. A little chubby. I'm hit with a dizzying sense of recognition, but I cannot place him. It's maddening. He stares at me, expression blank, apparently unaffected by the heat of the naked flames.

'Your first enemy. Tom Callum.'

The name is like a boot to the door of my memory, throwing light into a room I haven't even been near in...too long. Forever.

'Tom...' Remembering cowboys and Indians. Remembering cops and robbers. Stealing from a packed-lunch box in the cloak room. Blowing bubbles through a straw into milk, but...

'Tom wasn't my enemy! We were friends. He was my—' *my first best friend*, I think, but the figure is shaking his head.

'Tom was a bad friend. He disliked you. He used you to make himself feel better. You proved to him that he could get people to like him, and that's all you were to him. He treated you like his dog and thought of you like an insect.'

The words cut. The truth of them cuts. Still...

'He was a kid, I was a kid. I didn't know any of that, so where's the harm?'

The figure shrugs, an expression of elemental indifference. 'Tell me your choice.'

'My choice? What choice?'

He looks me in the eyes then, full bore, those dark eyes pinning me like a bug to a windscreen.

'Forgive or condemn?'

His eyes still hold me. I want to shake my head to clear it, but I can't look away. 'What difference does it make? What does my choice mean?'

His eyes leave mine, turning back to his closed fist. The answer is clear.

No more questions.

I shrug, and a shaky laugh comes out of me.

'OK, fine, fuck it, forgive. He was a boy, I don't care.'

The figure nods once. The fire roars, and the boy vanishes. As the flame lowers, another figure steps around the fire, the opposite side to where the boy had stood.

An older boy. Fat-faced. A small cluster of dark moles under his left nostril. Pasty white skin. My breath catches in my throat, and I feel a mini adrenaline spike. The last time I saw that face...

'Your second enemy. Stephen...'

'I know who he is. I know what he did.'

For a moment I think the figure is going to read out the

crime sheet anyway, like he doesn't have a choice but, for a mercy, he stays silent. Still, I smell blood; remember the taste of my own tears.

'Forgive or condemn?'

I feel my stomach roil, anger and dread. But he was just a boy, just a child, just young, just spoiled; not his fault. Then I remember his fists in my stomach, the look in his face. I remember feeling hate for the first time.

'Fuck him.'

I think the figure is going to get officious, demand the correct language, but he just nods again. The boy's expression does not change, and the fire roars, driving needles of heat and too-bright light into my eyes. I screw them shut reflexively, and when I open them again, Stephen is gone.

And so it goes. The enemies come, I pass judgment; they go. My first boss (forgiven), my first boyfriend (forgiven), my first boyfriend's girlfriend's sister (condemned), two more 'best friends' (condemned, both), strangers I never knew had hated me and harmed me, ex-lovers and ex-colleagues – and I forgive, forgive, forgive. I've lost track of time, of numbers.

The fire flares. I close my eyes, and when I open them, Sarah is there.

She's wearing the white nightdress she wore for so many years of our marriage. Her long black hair falls free, down to her waist, curling there. Her face is older than when we met, more careworn, but still striking, handsome, beautiful. No make-up. She stares ahead, blankly.

'I don't understand.'

'Sarah Locke.'

'I know who she is, I know my wife! But why...'

'She held you back.'

The accusation floors me completely.

'She feared you, and sought to control you because of

her fear. She learned to hide her fear, and the loathing underneath that fear, but she held you back. Kept you from fulfilling your true potential. Clipped your wings, your ambitions; held you in place—'

'No! No, she loved me, she...'

'She loved you. She feared you. She loathed you. She held you in place. She held you back.'

My eyes scan her face, looking for some note of confirmation or denial, but her features don't change, and I realise that she's not really here at all. I'm looking at a waxwork model, a replica. Instead, I reach within, and feel...

I feel resonance. It's awful, but I feel truth. I remember now, sleepless nights. I remember too, nights when the dreams came, dark and terrible, fading as I woke. I remember awaking with a feeling of dread crushing my chest.

It's true. He speaks truth. Something in her had tried to control me, hold me back, and yet...

'She loved me.'

Silence.

'Forgiven.'

I close my eyes as the fire flares. I don't want to see her go.

I open my eyes, already looking to the other side of the fire, wondering how many more I have to see, how many...

My thoughts freeze. The thing standing in front of me is enormous – maybe eight-feet tall – hulking, broad. It wears a brown felt hat, like a Fedora. The brim is pulled low, but the crescent shadow cannot fully conceal the fact that the creature has no nose. There are flickering pinpricks of reflected firelight in that shadow, where eyes would be. Below, there is grey-pink flesh; lumpen, glistening slightly, as though coated in some translucent fluid. The jaw is almost cartoonish in length, chin jutting;

an obscenity. Above sits the mouth, a lipless hole filled with black, pointed teeth, jagged and jumbled like that of a shark.

An ankle-length trench coat and large black boots cover the rest of the thing from view, except for one final detail: the hand-sized scalpel blades which protrude from the sleeves of the coat.

My sweat seems to turn chill in a second and, despite the heat of the fire, I shudder.

'Your penultimate enemy. The Teacher.'

'The…what the *fuck* is that?' I'm whispering, terrified that the figure will move, come to life, attack with those blades or those awful teeth.

'The Teacher.'

'I don't…I mean, I never…'

'No. You would remember.'

My nerves are jagged and raw, but I could still almost swear that was a joke. Maybe. 'Nonetheless, it was your enemy.'

'Why? How?'

'It hunts your kind. You had come to its attention, and it was on its way to you. Had it found you, it would have destroyed you.'

I take in the shape, mind not quite able to accept the physical fact of it, rebelling at the notion of this thing as real, even as the firelight bathes it in a yellow glow. *Your kind*…the phrase is like a bucket of cold water to the face. I feel mortal dread rise in me.

'I don't, I can't—'

'No. But you need only decide.'

I stare at it a little while longer. It meant my destruction, but I never saw it. The teeth, those blades…

'No. Condemn.'

The figure nods, the flame rises, the monster fades from view.

On the other side of the fire—

'Your final enemy. Your mortal enemy.'

He's exactly as I remember, the last time I saw him. I know this for sure, even as I realise I'm incapable of remembering that last sight, the last time we stood face to face. It's terrifying, the realisation of that; the implications. I feel my mind reeling, like some mooring is coming loose, a terrible strain on the roots of my thoughts, like something is being torn.

'Jacob Locke.'

'Son.' The word comes out as a sob. I'm aware I've spoken aloud, but it's as though it's happening to someone else, being reported to me through wires over some terrible distance. I float in a void, and across the darkness I feel my eyes move in their sockets, picking out the shape of my son's teenage face, lit by fire. Still some of that chubbiness about the face, even as the fur is starting to show on his upper lip. Those beautiful blue eyes. That brow, so quick to furrow when upset or angry, one of my gifts to him. Ah, Son, why are you here? I feel my eyes move again, taking in his frame, his clothes, T-shirt, shorts, white trainers. His T-shirt is stained, dark fluid on the yellow fabric. His left arm is also darkened. I start to feel a burning pain in my lower back. His fist is clenched. Another pain, higher. His fist is black, dripping with dark fluid. More pain now, in my side, upper back, I should be falling, but the pain is both real and unreal, there and not there.

Like him.

Like me.

I look up at the figure, aware that there are tears running down my face now. I feel pain, and a throbbing rage, dark and terrible, choking me.

He stares back, impassive.

'Make your last choice. Make it, and we will be on our way.'

I look back to my son. I see him, and there's a doubling

in my mind; he is my son, he is meat; I love him, I despise him; I am repulsed by him, I am repulsed by myself; I want...

'What happened?'

Nothing.

I want...

'WHAT AM I?'

Nothing.

I lower my head. The tears run down my nose, fall to the ground.

'I forgive.'

I feel the fire flare. I do not look up. It roars, high and bright and fierce, then dies away to a red glow. Only coals now, soon to fade entirely, red to grey to black.

Dying.

'It's time.'

I look up. The figure is already in the boat, reaching his hand out to me.

I take a step forwards, then stop.

'There's a price, isn't there?'

He looks back, and for a moment, I think he isn't going to answer.

'There's always a price.'

'Okay. But I'm not even going to discuss that until you get me across. Clear?'

He nods, solemn.

I take his hand, and step into the boat.

...Wow. Could The Teacher be The Enemy? This just gets weirder and weirder.

<INPUT ENDS>

<INPUT BEGINS>

Excited. A huge piece of information dropped into my lap today. At lunch.

I think...I think I've found a way.

People talk differently in the Officer's Lounge. More...freely, I suppose. Why not? We've all been through algorithmic vetting after all – no guests allowed. If you're eating in that room, you're 'in.' The system cannot be wrong.

Which is useful.

I don't know anyone yet, so I sit by myself. It looks like other areas have more than one Officer at my level, so they know each other that way. Makes sense, I guess – clearly the data-gathering is only a tiny part of what the Ministry is about. I'm wondering why that wasn't obvious to me before.

I'm clearly not very bright.

<You. Don't. Say.>

Anyhow. This lunchtime, a group of four men sat behind me. Talking about systems and redundancies. I couldn't follow most of it. Then one of them mentioned the 'emergency broadcast system,' and I just about dropped my spoon.

They were laughing about it, recalling that the only time it's been used was by accident, when someone they called 'A-LAF' ended up giving everyone the same dream on the same night. They were giggling about how they spent hours on constructing...well, constructing a way to plausibly explain it that wasn't the truth (a 'storrie' was the word they used, I think), so people wouldn't twig that the 'dream' had been a broadcast – only to gradually realise that nobody talked about their dreams anyway, so it never came out.

They were laughing really hard about that. One of them patted another on the back and said: 'See, C-ROK? Never let it be said you don't have a lot to live up to! Good old A-LAF!' They all laughed some more, though I noted with little surprise that C-ROK didn't seem quite as amused as his colleagues.

I remember how I felt as I heard the casualness with which they discussed their playing...no, their lie. As I remember it, I feel it still. It makes me feel ill. Feverish.

Anyway.

I got up to leave, meal half finished. I had to get a good look at C-ROK. He's old. Grey, thinning hair. Wrinkles. Watery blue eyes. Tall. Relaxed looking, despite his age. Like he's never really had to worry about anything.

Yeah, okay. I'm trying to hate him.

I have to. I may need to ask him about the emergency broadcast system, and when I ask him, I will need him to answer.

I don't want to think about that.

Anyway, there's no hurry. Maybe if I just keep sitting near him and his group of friends, I'll glean enough from them to be able to figure it out for myself.

Maybe. Hopefully.

Yeah.

Well, here's tonight's sample, let's see—

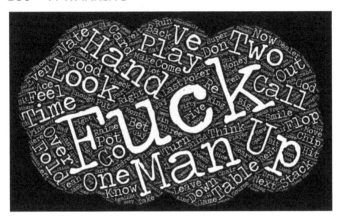

The rent is on the table, but that's okay. Because since I put it on the table, it's made friends with the next five months' rent – plucked out of the stacks of the other players and lined it up in front of me in neat multi-coloured piles. After a run of shitty luck that has all but defied belief; after heartbreak after heartbreak and loss after loss after motherfucking loss, the tide has fucking turned. I'm sweaty, stinky, and practically part of the chair – the fake-leather cushion moulded round my arse, sweat sticking my trousers to it through my pants, which are practically jammed up my crack. My balls are taking a Turkish bath but they don't itch. Not if I don't move, and I don't.

The throat of my shirt has been open for the last five hours, and the gallon and a half of Coke I've drunk means I can actually feel the hard pulse beating. I feel flushed, and I'm sure I look drunk. Fine by me; I'm in good company. Since I sat down at the £5/£10 'big game' table at 8 p.m. I've been faced by a parade of pissheads, losers, chancers, and drifters, all apparently with money to burn and possessing not even the most basic understanding of pot-odds, and *sweet Jesus* I love London town on a Friday night.

Not that it's been particularly kind to me since I

'turned pro' (sounds a lot better than 'got laid off and decided to gamble up my redundancy payoff', doesn't it? Yeah, I think so too). In fact, the poker gods have been pissing all over me, and the only part of me not stinking of urine would be my burning teeth— if you get me.

It's been a heart-breaking, heartburning, hair pulling bitch of a month, and by the time I sat down tonight I was way beyond last-chance saloon territory. The fucking rent was on the table, and really, there was the taste of blood in my throat and just a feeling of fuck you, things can't keep going like this. Stupid thinking. Loser thinking. My heart was pounding in my chest, and all I could think was to try and play snug as fuck, hit a couple of uncontested pots, build a little stack, quit with a win. Don't think about doubling up, or being all-in; just score a profit.

But it's fucking Friday night, so what are the chances? None whatsoever. I soon realise that there's a maniac three seats to my left, playing half his hands, raising loose early, limp calling, and because everyone else is clued into him, he's getting passengers every time, building nice big family pots and firing away at flops like his chips are on fire. Fucker's up too; two k buy-in max and he must have the best part of three and a half grand in front of him.

Fucker.

Course, the way he's winning means one of a couple of things – he's streaking, or he's up against scared money. Or a bit of both. I'm leaning to scared money. That's great news if I can shake him off and build a stack – I could run the table and make my nut easy – but that wasn't the plan, and anyway, if he's streaking that won't matter a gnat's fart in a hurricane, and I've only seen fifteen hands so that's no kind of sample size, but here I am just the same with pocket Queens in the cut-off, and he opens for fifty quid, and there's two callers to me. *God-fucking-dammit.*

I actually think about folding. Seriously. I count off the

two-fifty in chips. Look at the pile. Look at the five-fifty that leaves behind. If I make this bet and then have to fold the flop, I'm fucked. I can't make the rent, even if I leave straight afterwards.

On the other hand, that fucker's playing every other hand, and the others are all just trying to catch a flop. And I'll have position on him for the whole hand.

Jacks I think I would have mucked (bad beat stories are the most boring imaginable, so let me just stay I have three fish-hook horror stories from the last month that I won't forget if I live to be a hundred) but it's Queens, and if I can just take this arsehole down, the table is *mine*.

My luck has to change sometime. It just *has* to.

Besides, he might fold.

…

'Raise.'

I move the chips across the betting line slowly, deliberately. The blinds fold fast, but Mr Maniac doesn't even look up from under his cap to call.

Of fucking course.

The others fold. Dealer taps the table, mumbles 'heads up', and here comes the flop:

10 of Diamonds. 9 of Clubs. 2 of Spades.

He still doesn't look up as he checks.

And here we are. Just over five hundred in the pot, five-fifty in front of me, fifteen hands in, and I have exactly one move open to me. He took one glance at the flop, with affected indifference, and now he's just looking down at his hands folded over his cards. Not a lot there.

Shit, shit, shit.

Here's the problem. He tends to bet flops, this guy. Not one-hundred percent, but he's seen eight flops since I sat down, and he's bet five of them. No showdowns, so fuck really knows, right? But unless he's streaking like Jesus, I know he can bluff a flop.

He's not bluffing this one.

So, either he's scared of the new player, and it's a check fold...

Or he's trapping.

Back to the board. 2/9/10/rainbow. He's not going to be check calling with two overs and a flush draw, give me ulcers to the river, at least. Good. What does that leave? 7/8 for the open-ended straight draw? Jack/10 suited, beloved of all idiots who read Super/System once without really understanding it? Is he dumb enough to think he can trap here with top pair, shit kicker?

I look at him, at his stack, and glance round at the other players. Yes, he's that dumb.

Unfortunately, that hardly exhausts the possibilities. I could already be as good as dead – to 10/10, 9/9, 2/2 and, perhaps the worst possibility, some 10/9 draw that hit top two. Possible? Hell, *likely* given my luck to this day, practically a mortal fucking lock. At least I'm not worried about Aces, Kings, Ace/King – I know I'd have heard about it pre-flop - he's exactly the kind of turdmonkey that thinks people are too stupid to notice he raises a lot with crap but three-bets only with the goods.

So cut the over pair, we've got either fuck all that folds, 10/Jack to 10/Ace that calls (and I sweat out the turn and river), or two pair or the set, and I lose everything.

I don't have the time, inclination, or skill to calculate which of those is more likely statistically, but at least I know what I'm up against. Trivially obvious too that a check is as good as a fold. He moves on me regardless with the next card, and unless it's a Queen, I probably can't call.

I'd like to say that my thoughts were something macho like '*no guts, no glory*' but unfortunately, all I had left was '*fuck it.*'

'All in.'

Five hundred and fifty pounds in chips cross the line, and my hands shake not at all. My gut gurgles, my palms sweat, my heart fucking hammers in my ears like I'm going to have a fucking stroke, but I don't blush and my hands don't shake.

He looks up briefly, eyes not looking at me but the stack. Counting. I just start to exhale when he says:

'Call.'

I sit bolt upright, and the air leaves my lungs in a rush. Fuck. Fuck! I feel the room begin to draw away from me, my lips and face feel numb, like I'm retreating from the scene, having an out of body experience, and the dealer says

'Showdown. On their backs.'

from some impossible distance, and moving under their own power, my hands casually turn over my two ladies, face up on the green felt, and my opponent flips his hand, and there's not a gasp, but there is some kind of surprised reaction from the guy next to me, which I register as if from a faint radio broadcast on the edge of static, because the message coming back from my retina to my disbelieving brain is that my opponent has tabled pocket 8's.

I blink rapidly, expecting them to turn into 9's, the only thing that would make sense given my run, but they stubbornly stay 8's – lovely, lovely snowmen – and I notice a couple of grins on my right, like maybe some people have been waiting a while for this shoe to drop and they're glad, relieved even, to be at the felt when it happens. The dealer is quick enough that I barely have time for the pure elation of the moment to be diluted with anxiety about being out-drawn before he peels off a beautiful 4 of Spades on the turn and an irrelevant 7 of Hearts on the river, then indicates to me to take my winnings.

I rake the pot, tipping the dealer a £10 chip, and the world begins to wash back into focus. Next to me, a man remarks across the table to an acquaintance or friend,

'Because of course the raiser ALWAYS has Ace/King there, and just HAS to be bluffing the flop,' and his friend chuckles, and holy fuck if I don't chuckle too.

Holy mother of fucking God. I'm in the game.

My hands do shake, a little, as I stack my chips back up. Doubled up. Doubled up. Well okay, if I leave now, I've got two months' rent – or one month's rent and a roll to play the £1/£1 game again. Seat fee already came out of my pocket, so it's all profit.

I turn to the guy next to me. 'Things that you promise yourself you won't do when you sit down...' Sideways smile. Suddenly easy to smile, now.

'Don't work like that, do it? Gotta play the cards, man. Nice hand.' He smiles back; the relaxed, easy smile of the casual gambler, of a man that's never had his rent riding on the turn of a card, but that's cool, I'm grateful for the show of friendship, and all of a sudden I'm relaxed and ready to play some poker.

Which is handy, because suddenly the hands are flying thick and fast, like the poker gods turned on the good-card spigot.

Two circuits later, turdmonkey – angry and dispirited – tries a cute minimum re-raise pre-flop, and I snap-fold my steal bluff. He shows the Aces, pissed, and the very next hand he calls my button raise (three limpers, so I make it a hundred to go with cowboys) from the blinds. Everyone else folds out and the flop comes 2/8/4, Diamonds and Spades. I have no flush draw, so bet out one-seven-five into the two-fifty pot. He calls, turn's the 8 of Spades, two flush draws now – check, check, river the third 8. He bets two-fifty. I think about it, but not for long. Shove, call, King/King beats 10/10, and I've doubled up twice through the same guy, and now have the best part of three grand in front of me.

It's a blur, now – the cards, the hands, the opponents. Turdmonkey leaves, so do a couple of regulars; my opposition gets younger, drunker, more aggressive. I seem to float serenely above it all – knowing when to bluff, when to value bet, when to trap check – it seems like whatever I did last time, the cards give me the opposite, most deceitful hand next time. My stack is big enough that I'm protected now against all-comers, their two k max buy-in can damage but not kill me, and pretty soon, as the chips pile up, they can't even really do that. I fly clean through the four k barrier with an incredible three-barrel bluff against someone who just will not put two grand in with top pair against someone running like God, and I hit six thou with a flopped house – pocket 9's on a 9/King/King flop. Against Ace/King.

Heaven.

Dragging that pot, I become aware for the first time of an ache behind my eyes. The amount of Coke I've necked means that I'm unlikely to feel tired for several days, but I'm definitely starting to hit that uncomfortably sweaty, stretched feeling that caffeine plus sugar, plus adrenaline, plus physical inactivity creates. The table is thinning out too, finally; the two players I just felted are not replaced by fresh blood. We're down to six, and two of them (a super-tight Asian gentleman and a tired, bored-looking black man) are both yawning with an ostentation that strongly indicates the game doesn't have long left to run. Probably they'd have left already if not for the siren call of my out-sized stack, and the feeling that sooner or later, my streak has to break.

Not happening fellas, I think, but I'm happy for them to keep firing. Tonight, I'm fucking Superman. Bulletproof.

That's the moment that a hand slaps me on the back, hard, and I jolt in my chair, heart suddenly hammering very uncomfortably. My hands spasm, and I knock half my stack all over the felt. I hear a burst of wheezy laughter that I'd recognise anywhere, carried over my shoulder on a heavy breeze of fetid, whisky-soaked breath.

Fucking Nate.

Fuck it.

'You doin' all right man? Hey, fuck me, y'are! Yer fuckin killin' it, man! Fair fuckin play, look at you man; fuckin killin' it! Fuck!'

It's possible he's not entirely sober.

'Hey, Nate.'

'Hey yourself! Didn't tell me you was out tonight, ya fucker! Keepin' all the fish to yerself, yeah? Jammy cunt!'

He doesn't mean to be offensive. I'm almost certain of it.

'Yeah, look—'

'Yeah, what's that you got man, five fuckin grand? Didn't even know you played this high man, thought you were strictly one and one!' Another burst of laughter – I actually feel a fine spray of his saliva splash my cheek. My stomach does a slow flip.

Please God, don't let this perfect poker evening end with me puking on my chips.

'Nate! Yeah, man, just decided to take a shot, you know? Felt lucky.'

Self-depreciating. Apologetic. Please-go-away-and-leave-me-alone.

More of that fucking laugh, practically roaring in my ear now. Jesus, he whiffs so bad I can smell him over my own stink. If he doesn't move soon, get his sweaty hand off my back, I think I really am going to throw up.

'Fucking lucky? No shit man, you fucking cleaned up! Lucky I came along; you almost had it your own way all fucking night!'

What? Oh, fuck me, no, no, no, no...

'Hit that fucking accumulator yesterday. Been on the piss ever since.'

Voice travelling to my left, he's moving towards the empty chair.

No no no no no...

'Fuck it, easy come, easy go, right? Let's play some fucking cards.'

An obscene wedge of bills hits the felt as he sits down. I stare at it, stupidly, temporarily unable to process what is happening.

'Naw, Nate, look—'

'Don't worry, man, don't sweat! Like I said, it's whatchacallit. Found money! Ain't gonna miss it!'

Yeah, because *that's* what I'm worried about, Fuckstick.

'Honest, Nate, I was going to leave soon, I'm fucking knackered...'

This time the spit spray from the laugh goes all over his money (and I see a flicker of disgust cross the face of the dealer, too quick for Nate to notice) and the clip on my shoulder is enough to almost knock me off my chair, and as I flail and grab the edge of the table the other half of my stack spills over.

Motherfucker.

'Gonna fucking leave! Fucking good one, mate!'

He turns to mister super-tight, who has been observing this exchange with polite disbelief.

'This fucking degenerate's gonna leave while I'm putting the big cheddar down! Fucking comedi*enne*, right? Good one, man.'

I see the clip coming this time. Brace. It helps a bit.

'Naw, man, come on. Let's play some fucking POKER!'

The dealer has counted out the cash on the table quickly, and in the polite, measured tone of one experienced in delivering bad news to the intoxicated, says 'Sorry, sir, but I'm afraid you've exceeded the table limit. You've got four thousand, five hundred and eighty pounds here. Maximum buy-in is two thousand.'

Thank you, sweet Jesus. Of course he can't put down

enough to stack me. Okay, fine, play with the pisshead for a little bit, let him run the table and his mouth, and beg off once he wins a couple of pots. Better yet, let one of the others stack him. Play super-snug and get the fuck home with your stack and honour intact, for tomorrow is another day. No need to take him on, no need to engage.

'Unless, of course, no one objects to raising the table limit?'

Oh no, you fucking didn't.

But of course, he did. And of course, mister super-tight (who's already dreaming about stacking this guy pre-flop with Aces, clearly with no fucking idea what he's up against) is eagerly indicating his supreme lack of a problem with this notion, and so it goes around the table, eager happy nods, *please let the nice drunk man sit down with his huge amounts of gambling money at stakes way above his normal limit, that would be quite fine, I'm suddenly not tired at all*, and by the time the dealer's gaze turns to me (did I see a flicker of sympathy there? Probably not) the mood of the table is very clear.

Oh fuck this.

I nearly say no anyway, 'cause just fuck this noise; I nearly just get up and leave, rack my chips and go, but they're all looking at me, with various degrees of 'do-not-tap-the-glass' in their eyes, and *fuck, fuck, fuck it*, I'm just fucked.

Exhale.

'No problem.'

Smiles all round. Nate nodding like it's a formality. A better man might feel some sympathy for what these poor saps have just unleashed on themselves. Not me. Rage, bile, and hatred clog up my throat like a physical thing. I'm choking on it, and I just want to kill every last retarded one of them, and then myself, because Nate just sat down with the best part of a five grand stack, so let the poker holocaust commence.

Not me, you fuck (I vow, again.) *Not me, not this time.*
'Let's play some fucking CARDS!'

Big grin. Red faced, barely able to focus, practically swaying in his chair. It's no act either – I've been in the hell of this man's orbit long enough to know that. He does know a bit about poker, he's not a moron, but he's insanely aggressive and painfully lucky and I've seen him go broke many, many times...but he always fucking kills me. Every time. My fucking kryptonite.

I sweep my cards into my fist, miserably, all the good feelings of the night evaporating, the rush and the poker gods abandoning me – I actually feel them leave – and I try to mentally hunker down, calm my jangling nerves. Try really hard to just play some smart poker and get out with my stack intact.

Six month's rent and change. Get it home. Somehow, get it home. Just avoid this prick.

But it's impossible. He raises every hand. No shit. A hundred to go.

Blind.

Every hand.

The other players start to look nervous as well as excited, like they realise they're in what we like to call a high-variance situation. Lots of folds, lots of respect. That lasts for two circuits, twelve miserable hands where it's raise, fold, fold, fold, fold, take your money, and finally Mr super-tight wakes up in position with something good and calls the raise. We all know the score and get the fuck out of the way.

Flop 10/8/4 rainbow. Nate belches, then slurs 'Bet,' and throws three hundred into the pot. Super-tight snap-shoves, overexcited, already counting his money. Nate deliberates, hope warring with reason, which ends exactly how you'd predict:

'Call.'

The cards hit the felt. Super-tight caught cowboys.

Nate tables 7/3. Off. Super-tight does not smile. It's like he knows. I sure as fuck do.

Turn is a Jack. The river brings the 9.

Runner/runner straight for the win.

Super-tight stands up so fast, his chair almost falls over. He's done for the night. He thrusts his hand out in congratulations, smile sick and pained. 'Nice hand, sir.'

Nate barely touches the outstretched hand. 'Thanks.' Serves him fucking right, I think.

Then I realise, with a sinking feeling in my bowels that, with the additional chips, Nate now has me covered.

One hand could cost me everything.

The rage comes back then, helpless, powerful, but there's a new component to it – the desire for vengeance. This man has tormented me mercilessly, been the bane of my fucking life the last month, a living, breathing totem of bad fucking luck, and all of a sudden, I've had enough, and I'm glad we're playing for keeps.

Because tonight, it's going to be different. Tonight, I'm going to fuck him up for good. Found money, Nate? Fine. Finders fucking keepers.

'Nice hand, Nate.'

He smiles. 'Yeah, I just felt it was coming, you know?'

'I do indeed, Nate. I do indeed.'

I manage a smile. It even feels genuine, in its way.

We're back down to six, but the other players very quickly become non-entities, recognising somehow the battle that is about to commence.

Next hand, he comes out with the standard hundred raise, I make it a thousand. Blind. He looks up at me then, regarding me with an attempt at care, and I remember with a nasty jolt that this man is not quite as stupid as he looks. If only because that wouldn't be medically possible.

'Caught a hand, did you mate?' He hates to fold pre-flop. It's practically against his religion. But he does, and I flip over my hand indifferently as I reach for the pot.

Turns out I had Jack/3 off-suit – I was hoping for 7/2, but it's enough to send a message. The others, who have watched me build this stack over several hours with great care, are agog. Let 'em be. I'm only playing one guy now.

There's a thunderstruck pause, followed by an explosion of laughter so violent that the dealer flinches. I look over, and yes, Nate has flushed an alarming brick red, the vein in his forehead is throbbing, and he's pounding the table hard enough to make his chips dance and tumble.

Eventually he manages to catch enough breath to say 'Came to play, did you? Came to fucking play! Like it man, like it. Beautiful.'

He seems genuinely pleased. I'm feeling pretty happy myself. Next hand, and he's first to act against my big blind.

'All in blind!' Happy with himself. Ecstatic, even. Flushed, sweating freely, stinking. I've seen him like this before, and I know for sure he won't stop 'till he goes broke, or we do.

Fine by me – tonight, it's gonna be fucking him. The others all check their hands, and fold disappointedly, and it comes down to me.

'Come on, call blind man! G'wan man, you know you want to!'

'Can't, man,' I say with a regretful smile, and peak at my hand.

King of Clubs, Queen of Hearts.

Interesting.

I put a chip on top of my cards to keep them safe, and look over at my opponent.

This is it. It has to be, right? I mean, he's blind, so any hand significantly above average, I just have to call, right? Fucking crazy, but that's poker, right? That's what this whole evening has been about, yeah? The poker gods putting me in this spot, to finally end the torment, once and for all.

'Fuck me, he's actually thinking about it! Hahahahaha! I fucking love you mate, I really do!'

And yeah, what the fuck am I thinking about? I've got six thousand pounds in front of me, from a lowly seven-fifty start, and if ever there was a time to give up, get up, and go home, this must surely be it.

But...

But, I have him beat, statistically. Crushed, even. Statistically, this is the right call, an easy call. Be offered this bet a thousand times, take it every time, and never have to work again. Right? This is poker; it's the nature of the game, how good players make money off bad ones. Knowing the odds and playing them.

This is the game.

Six fucking grand.

There's a sickening inevitability about it, isn't there? It feels like there is.

Fuck it, if I go broke, I'm just gonna quit, use the next two weeks to get a job, burn all the books and never look back.

It's a relief, this thought – the pressure seems to evaporate. Make the right decision, to go with all the unrewarded correct decisions I've made this month, and let the poker gods decide. Fuck it. Last time pays for all.

My heart is perfectly calm, my hands steady. I come out of my own internal processes enough to realise the room is silent, everyone is staring at me – even fucking Nate has shut up, and is looking – dear God, is he looking nervous? Could it possibly be he's suddenly woken up to the stupidity of this situation? Might it not just be that under the drunken bravado, a game was being played, and now there's a fear we're off script? I fucking hope so. I do. I smile into his ruddy, sweaty, fat face.

Last time pays for all.

'Call.'

...Well. What the fuck was *that* all about?

<INPUT ENDS>

<INPUT BEGINS>

They know about the machine! The flash came to me personally, via my desk com at work. 'Be on the lookout; experimental recovery device; blah blah...' - can't believe they are trying to claim it's *post*War tech. Ridiculous; it's clearly far in advance of anything *we* could possibly bolt together - '...believed to be misplaced in one of the data-storage device warehouses. Item extremely dangerous, do not approach – flag to orange band clearance or higher. Interference with the device is punishable.' That last is not uncommon, but they'd normally offer a small bonus as a reward. I guess they are really worried about someone getting their hands on it; figuring out how it works.

I can see why.

Only trouble is, it means I'm running out of time. If they know about it, they'll figure out that it's been taken eventually. Then all they have to do is check the key card access logs for the warehouse, do a door-to-door of all the residences...

So. I'm sorry, but I'm afraid I'm going to have to do something pretty drastic in order to get this out to you.

I'm not looking forward to it, but I have to get this information out before they catch me. It's too important.

But I can't do anything tonight, so might as well run samples. Starting with—

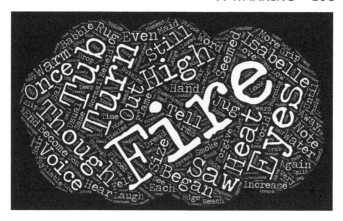

So, you would have my confession? Very well, I give it freely. Still, I beg you, do not interrupt with your confounded questions, though I know you will have many. Save them until the end. That which I must tell, I would tell once through, lest I lose my nerve. Attend then, and transcribe faithfully.

It was a normal Wednesday evening. I had completed work in my study at the usual hour, and taken my supper with Isabelle. She was her usual delightful self – questioning, laughing, the spirit of gaiety alive in her shining eyes and rosy cheeks...

...Forgive me.

The tub had been prepared as normal: the large basin placed by the roaring fire, the water pleasantly warm but not hot. After our meal, Isabelle and I retired to the living room. The maid was dismissed, and Isabelle allowed me to disrobe her, giggling as I tickled her naked arms, squealing with delight when my whiskers tickled her belly.

She loved to laugh.

I lifted her into the tub and bathed her, talking to her as I did so about my day. I let her splash a little, watched her spread out and pretend to swim, my arms leaning on the edge of the tub, waiting to reach in and grasp her if she were to slip.

I washed her hair with soap, then blew some bubbles between my thumb and forefinger, her high voice encouraging me to increase their size, her laughter flowing like some sweet warming nectar.

I had turned to the fire, reaching for a jug of clean water to rinse her hair with, when the change occurred. When I turned away, she had been excitedly describing the bubbles, remarking on their sizes. This had continued as I turned, but as my hand neared the handle of the jug, her voice transformed. Mid-word it dropped, first low then high, then low, alternating with each syllable. At the same time, the words vanished, replaced by a nonsensical babble.

'Da-BOO-Rah-JAK-ka-SAL-Ood.'

Each lower register seemed deeper than the last, each high note louder and shriller. I cannot fully put into words the terror that struck me in this moment; how horrified I was by that apparently senseless noise. Something in the alternating register, the apparently random sounds, struck dread into me as though I were hearing some awful incantation.

As if in sympathy with my panic, the large log in the centre of the fire split with a loud crack. Smoking embers flew into the deep rug and began to smoulder.

'Joh-RAY-Lin-GAR-Den-DOO-Sal-REF-Mal...'

'Isabelle! Stop!'

I was still looking towards the fireplace, attention caught by the tendrils of smoke rising from the rug, and my panic gave my voice a timbre and gruffness that would ordinarily command obedience, possibly even tears. I had a moment to curse my own harshness, to wonder at why I should be so gripped with emotion as to address her so harshly.

Then the babble rose again.

As I close my eyes now, I hear it still, every dread

syllable. But I dare not repeat it. Suffice it to say, her voice deepened further, hitting notes that were surely not possible, and the high notes became screeches that grated my senses raw. The flames in the fire began to surge, burning hotter, the coals glowing fiercely. The smoke from the rug was becoming thicker, darker, and I saw flame there begin to flicker.

In a spasm of movement, I grabbed one of the jugs and poured it out over the smouldering rug with a cry.

At the same time I felt the heat from the fire increase again, becoming more intense, seemingly drawn into ferocity by the inhuman noises my darling daughter was producing, though in truth by then I scarcely recognised her voice. My gaze returned to the fire, eyes squinting against the heat, and there I saw...

There I saw the fire, receding and growing, falling back and away. The fireplace around it grew faint and faded, then the ground on which it sat sunk too, as though melting in the heat— DON'T LOOK AT ME LIKE THAT!

DON'T!

...

Forgive me. Forgive me. It— No, no, you weren't there. Let me tell it, quickly.

The ground fell away before my unbelieving eyes, until I was kneeling upon a pillar of rock, surrounded on all sides by darkness, and a sheer drop. Far beneath me, as far as my eyes could see, fire spread in all directions, flickering and rolling. The babble had become a chant, the deep parts guttural as a mad dog, the high notes shrieking like a bird of prey, the devilish syllables seeming to warp my mind as surely as they warped the world around us. Boiling waves of heat rose from the pit, singeing my eyebrows, burning the very air in my throat.

My head turned back to the tub, seemingly of its own volition, and I beheld her.

Her skin had turned red, and her eyes glowed a sickly yellow, as though lit from inside by a flame burning some noxious substance. Her smile had become a leer of perfect depravity, pointed teeth pushing out at crazed angles from bloody gums, her lips splitting in places as the grin pushed her mouth unnaturally wide, as though whatever was passing through her by invocation was tearing her apart as it transformed her. I beheld her but knew her not, and when her eyes met mine, I saw only damnation; mine, hers, perhaps the world's.

I acted on pure instinct. Though her size had increased somewhat, she was still an infant in basic form, so it was a simple matter to grab her legs and pull. Her red skin was almost painfully warm to the touch, but my grip held firm, and her head slipped beneath the surface of the water with ease.

I shifted my body, moving my hands to hold her shoulders, fearing that mouth, those teeth. I saw understanding dawn across that hideous visage, and then a ferocious rage that seemed almost to stab out at me; certainly I felt my heart lurch in my chest, but the fear that had galvanised me to action held me in its grip, and I maintained the downward pressure as the monster began to thrash.

How it struggled! The water churned and roiled as I wrestled with the inhuman figure. It seemed to last an age, long enough for me to wonder if perhaps this dread creature could somehow breathe underwater, but gradually the struggles began to lessen and I felt the awesome heat begin to dissipate, to withdraw. I perceived at the edge of my vision that the world was assuming its rightful shape once more, even as the creature in my hand began to shrink, to fade from that hellish bloody hue to the soft pastel-pink of my beloved Isabelle.

I beheld her there, once again perfect. My darling daughter. She lay at the bottom of the tub, beyond all pain, all misery, all love. At peace.

I sobbed for a while, before ringing for the maid. She in turn called for the constabulary, and there you found me.

This is my story. I will not tell it again. Do as you must, as your conscience and laws dictate. I pray only that the end be swift, and that afterwards I see her restored. That I might hear that beautiful laugh once more.

I desire nothing else.

...Aww f—

<INPUT ENDS>

<INPUT BEGINS>

Sorry, sorry. I just don't know what— Was that a brain dump from someone in the throes of a delusion? But then, it felt almost dictated...of course! It was the brain dump of a *witness* to the confession! Okay, okay. Still...

The chickens. That blind invasion piece. Ted. There's so much more to the world than we've been led to believe...

No more. No more hesitations. Time is running out. I have to find out how to do the emergency broadcast.

Tomorrow, I'll pay C-ROK a visit at his accommodation.

<INPUT ENDS>

<INPUT BEGINS>

Well, I did it. Followed C-ROK home. Got in the door. Beat him – hurt him pretty badly. Got what I needed: the emergency broadcast protocols. How to send to the brain dumps remotely. There's even a specific setting that allows broadcast only to citizens. I can't imagine why they'd want that capacity – or maybe I just don't want to.

Doesn't matter. It exists, and now I know how to use it. I'll need to get inside the comms building, but I have a pass now, so that won't be hard.

At least not until C-ROK turns up missing.

I got him to send a message saying he was ill. That should buy me some time. Suppose I should thank them for teaching me about 'lying.' There's a kind of justice to it, I think, though it still made me sick to my stomach. Still, I have two or three days, now. I really should just get this out to you. Only...

Well, I want to try to hide the machine, that's one thing. If I can get it hidden, somewhere they won't think to look...Look, I just don't want it to get destroyed before you can get your hands on it. So there's that, too.

Also, well, I have a few samples left. Seems imprudent not to run them. Just in case.

But not tonight. I'm too—
Just not tonight

<INPUT ENDS>

<INPUT BEGINS>

Can't sleep. Nightmares. Listen, when they find him, when you hear what I did...that wasn't me, okay. I wasn't...I didn't— Fuck. I mean, he was scared. C-ROK, he was...but I didn't— I did what I had to, to get this out. I didn't—

Oh shit, he was so *scared*. *So* scared, I just...
But I HAD to. I had to. I...

I had to.
For you.
I'm sorry. Fuck, I'm sorry.

<INPUT ENDS>

<INPUT BEGINS>

Replayed last night. Sorry. Again. That was just...Sorry. Delayed reaction. I did what I had to do.

Today was hard. I actually did the job I was supposed to do, for the first time since I was appointed. Nothing to it, of course – a lot of staring at changing numbers and unchanging green lights. Really, it's so odd that I'd never even thought about what she did, before I— Before she— I just assumed – I don't know, that it was important and difficult. The secrecy and separation is so much a part of every day, I hadn't even *thought about* how I hadn't even thought about it.

Is that part of how they get away with this whole thing? They tell us without telling us; make us fearful, secretive...

I don't know. I don't know what I'm talking about any more. Never mind. I have three samples left to run. Might as well get it done as soon as possible. Before they find C-ROK.

Okay, what have we g—

I drop the package on my boss's desk, and the wax paper doesn't do much to muffle the splat. I look up at him, smiling, suppressing the tremor of déjà vu that runs down my spine.

'What the fuck is this?'

Not the response I was hoping for.

'Kennedy's brain, sir. As requested.'

He looks blank. But then he does that a lot – it's the stress of the job, trying to hold the big picture in his mind. It'd drive anybody crazy.

'Getting it out of the autopsy room was a snap. Psy-dev were spot on – nobody even looks at the nurse. So that's one mystery they'll never solve...'

I trail off, uncertain. His face has gone from blank to confused and is now clear into anger, but that's not why I stop. It's because there's something wrong with the paint on the wall behind him. It's faded, grubby. Last time I'd been here, it had still been fresh enough to smell. What the—?

'Hitler's body?'

I blink rapidly.

'Boss?'

'I sent you out for Hitler's body, you bring me back—is this really Kennedy's brain? It smells funny…'

'Boss, that was days ago!' I flash back to the rubble outside the bunker, the smell of burning and concrete dust that infused the air, the warmth of the flames from the shallow ditch in the ground...

'No, it was fifteen minutes ago! I'm glad you're back, though; there's been some kind of fuck up with World War One causality...'

I feel the blood drain from my face.

'Boss, what's the date?'

He tells me.

'I need to hide!'

'What's—'

'No time! I'm coming!'

I push him hard in the chest, sending his chair rolling back from his desk, and dive across it. Over the thump of his chair hitting the wall, I can hear footsteps in the hall outside – my footsteps. I reach back up to grab the brain, then I remember the conversation I had; I leave it in place and dive back under.

My boss is staring at me crouched in the alcove of his desk, total confusion on his face. Then the door opens and he looks up, and I see a fantastic amount of emotional reaction happen in a very short time, and I hear myself saying 'Are you okay, sir?'

And I have time to marvel at the calmness of his voice as he says 'Fine, fine. How was Berlin?'

'Bloody grim, to be honest with you...'

It's an excruciating experience, hearing my own voice, so I burrow my thumbs into my ears and wait it out. I find myself replaying it in my mind anyway; him laying out the problem with Archduke Ferdinand's travel schedule, some potential diary clash that might prevent his assassination, blah, blah, blah. I remember the crack I made about how bad his sandwich smelt as I left (sure, *now* I remember why the package had given me such a sense of déjà vu, even back in Dallas when I was wrapping it up, waiting for the jump back). Finally, he pushes his seat back. I take my fingers from out of my ears, cringing at the sound of my own departing footsteps.

My boss is at the door, locking it. I stand, brushing dust off my pant suit – *Jesus, doesn't anyone ever clean around here?* – and when I look up again, it takes me a second to register the gun in his hand.

I go very still.

'Boss?'

He looks sad, but not even a little hesitant.

'Sorry, Sid.'

In a flash, I understand the dark stain on his wall that had been there during the Lucan briefing, and the fresh paint after faking the Soviet records (after we'd found out Hitler's body was never supposed to go missing in the first place). The déjà vu feels like it's rattling my skull, and I just have time to blurt out 'You can't! I'm not supposed to be here! This isn't supposed to be possible!'

His face is impassive.

'You said it, kid.'

He pulls the trigger.

...I can't make any sense of that. None whatsoever. I hope you can.

These short, intense bursts...I wonder if the machine is running down somehow. Head is pounding now, face dripping sweat. Going to have to call it a night.

<INPUT ENDS>

<INPUT BEGINS>

I'm running out of time, as well as samples. I spent most of the day looking over my shoulder, worried that someone was going to grab me, take me back into the interview room. No alerts. They still haven't found C-ROK. Guess the illness report worked.

Still, I have to get on with it. Tonight is the night. Tonight, I'll broadcast all of this out, and you'll...well, I hope you'll see clearly for the first time in your lives. Understand that The Ministry is not working in your best interests. Rise up! Seize the mainframe! Find out the truth for yourselves.

I believe in you. I believe in your capacity to be powerful. To be better than this corrupt regime. To be fearless in seeking out the truth and reclaiming your history – your *real* history, not the lies they've been shoving into your minds.

But I'm getting ahead of myself. Two more samples. Two more data points. Better run them, while I still—

I'm moving through the final preparations for detonation. In the core of this gigantic station (current occupancy: one - me) is a three trillion gigaton fusion bomb. Called Larry.

It's big.

My name is Fred, and I'm a Solar Engineer – the best in the business – and in just over two hours, I'm going to detonate Larry. It's one of only ten in existence, and the only one to ever be used. It's quite an honour. When it explodes, we will be close enough to the sun to induce supernova, followed by collapse. The shockwave from the blast will vaporise everything within the solar system right through to Pluto. That's just from the bomb; the sun exploding will superheat the ashes of Earth at least, probably Mars too.

I adjust some dials, tweak some wiring. Recheck the safeguards.

Preparing for the final setting of the sun.

It has to be a manual detonation, of course. It's too important that the positioning be precise, and that the explosion not happen prematurely. The chances of the device being accidentally triggered by microwave transmission is pretty remote, what with the current levels of encoding, but given the size of the bang, 'pretty remote' wasn't quite enough of a guarantee for the Clients. Understandably.

I wonder what being consumed in the blast – atomised, to be precise – will feel like. I ran some calculations before arriving, and was faintly surprised to note that my death will actually set a record – it will be the quickest ever recorded. Still, all that stuff about time slowing down, your life passing before your eyes...

I've never died, you see. I've visited the clone tanks, and I know the model that I'm going to be uploaded into. I can feel the faint tickle behind my eyes from the uploader, in point of fact, as it streams my consciousness and memories out to the Vault for storage. I remember the surgeon who oversaw the fitting, kind grey eyes behind the mask, a rasping voice explaining how the whole process would work, while I tried to look calm. It's been standard tech for centuries now; tried, tested, and true, but still...I've never had to use it. And I'm nervous.

I keep myself busy – there are always settings to check, miniscule course corrections to observe, and failsafe after failsafe to cycle through. It helps a little. The part of my mind that stays distracted, I try to refocus on the reward side of things. The Clients are legendary providers, after all. I should get at least a planet out of it – maybe even a small system. I'd like binary suns, I think, just two or three planets to manage. Nothing too onerous.

I read through the subroutine report. Temperature modifiers stable, heat shields fully functional – even this close to the sun, the internal temperature of the station is cool enough for me to need clothes. All the sensor streams are live, broadcasting all the lovely images and data the Clients have paid so much money for – data that will go some way to defraying the cost of the exercise. They will tell the universe that that was the reason – knowledge, the quest for ever-greater understanding. Some of the Clients may even believe it. Me, I'm pretty sure they're just doing it because they can, and because it amuses them. Who wouldn't want to see the world burn?

A quick shudder passes through me. I refocus on the info stream. Engines fine; energy levels optimal; 'lifestream' data transmitting. There was a 0.4 nanosecond blip in the teleportation barrier, probably caused by a solar flare, but it's no risk – this system has been clear for over a decade, and the kind of tech needed to exploit a window that small lies only in the hands of the Clients. Which, given they're paying for this whole thing...

I close my eyes and lean back in my chair, trying to relax. The image that comes to mind is the bank of Petra clones I'd seen on my tour of the facility. I'd encountered her via the holo-vids, of course, even paid extra for dream implants once or twice, but it occurred to me now that, after completing this job, I could own one. Or, well, as many as I wanted, really.

Quite a thought. I picture her floating, naked form, recall the dreams, and I wonder...

'Don't fucking move.'

The voice is male, the tone conversational, civil even, but there is an unmistakable note of authority. The cold metal against my Adam's apple makes its own rather forceful case. I obey, keeping my eyes closed, though regretfully the visions of Petra flee immediately.

I feel my seat being moved away from the control console. I hear the sound of buttons clicking. Suddenly there's movement all around me, people moving in different directions, at least five, all seemingly talking at once, words babbling together:

'...the upload links in place, I need...'

'...sure the signal spoof is up, we have to...'

'...the station scanner, if we don't...'

'...path data too early, they'll know...'

'...WHERE'S MY FUCKING SPOOF?'

'...twenty seconds, Relax! I've...'

'...systems normal, repeat, all coolant...'

'...only transmissions are what we want them to...'

'...get that alarm system offline! Why risk...'

'...Ten seconds to Spoof!'

'...you make sure the teleport shield is back up, we don't want...'

'...phase batteries will cycle down, but we need...'

'...pass me that? I need...'

Then a whiff of perfume comes to me from my dream. Unmistakable. I feel my heart start to beat faster, even in the middle of all the terror and confusion.

'...Petra! Come here, I need...'

'...megacycles, these idiots...'

'...Spoof is up! We are invisible!'

'...and try and stop perspiring, will you? It's deeply distracting...'

'You love it!'

That voice.

Then another.

'All right everybody, phase one complete. Take a moment, then move to your assigned position and role.'

The gravelly tone and the shock of recognition are too great, and my eyes spring open.

He's standing facing me. Same tall frame, short grey curly hair, those same kind grey eyes. His lower jaw is wrinkled and it gives him a gaunt look, harsher than the eyes suggested, but it's definitely—

'Doctor Murphy!'

His eyes switch focus and he looks at me, holds my gaze.

'Hi, Fred. Sorry about this.'

'I told you not to move!' Hot breath blows in my ear, and I feel the blade increase pressure on my throat. I whimper. The doctor's eyes move away from me again, looking over my shoulder.

'No need for that. I surprised him, that's all. Should have realised that would happen. Let him talk, if he wants to.'

His eyes return to mine. He tries a smile. It's not reassuring.

'It's okay, Fred. All be over soon.'

I feel my stomach roll over lazily. I wonder if I'm going to puke.

'There's been a change of plan, that's all.'

Behind me, I can hear hyper-jump calculations being made and cross-checked.

I discover something interesting, something that might under other circumstances be useful: there are so many impossible things happening at once that I am able to just let go and allow my mind to focus on what seems to be the most salient point.

'You're trying to steal the bomb?'

'Oh, we're not trying.' That wintery smile again, there and gone. 'Once we complete the calculations, the bomb is ours.'

'But...' Too many questions, too little time. How long will it take them to make the calculations? Five minutes? Three? Depending on the destination. And...

'...but there's no jump drive on the station! I mean there was, but—'

'...it was removed. As a safety precaution. Quite right too, a sensible move. Or it would be, if they'd actually done it.'

'But, I saw it was gone! I saw...'

A slow shake of the head.

'You saw what the machines showed you. They all did.'

My mind is reeling, racing, on fire. An inside job?

'This is Client on Client?'

'You'd think so, wouldn't you? I suppose technically that's true, yes. But none of us think of ourselves as them.'

I hear a cold anger at this last. It scares me more than the blade at my neck.

The seconds are flying by now. Thirty? At least. My heart is thudding hard and fast. He reads my face.

'Go on, ask.'

'The fail-safe! The tracers. As soon as anything on board deviates from the expected path, they'll just flick the switch, depressurise the station...'

'We've deactivated the triggers and spoofed the trace signal. They won't know we've moved until it's done.'

It's too much to take in. I've heard rumours of Client on Client conflict, but it never, ever goes public. But this...

'It's too big! Even if you pull it off, they won't be able to cover it up.'

No smiles now as he replies: 'Correct.'

'But, ah, you'll, I mean...'

He cocks an eyebrow.

'They'll send you to Hell! No offence, but I mean they will. You'll...'

I can't finish. The images are too horrible.

'No, they won't.'

'They will! They'll catch you—'

'No. By the time they know Larry is missing, we will both be gone, and Hell will be off-line. Permanently.'

'You— You're going to destroy Hell?'

He actually laughs at that, a single sharp sound, almost spoken.

'Oh, I think we can do a little better than that. No, we're going after the Vault.'

He lets it settle in. The enormity of it. My mind reels, trying to keep up with the new information, trying to understand. Of course; destroy the Vault and you'd certainly shut down Hell – no way to keep punishing the condemned if you can't keep downloading them to new clones – but still...

'You'll kill millions of people!'

'Not quite. The Vault is well-protected enough that even Larry won't destroy it completely. But the blast will send it a long way in an unpredictable direction, and the fallout will scramble the output signals for decades. Hopefully centuries.'

I'm stunned into silence. I actually feel my jaw go slack with shock. I remember the last time the up-link went down. The horror stories. The 'lifestream' data decays so rapidly. Near-instant upload is needed to the clones to prevent...degradation. The ones who were only trapped for a few minutes were okay, with rehabilitation, but the rest...

The loss of personality, of self, of language – the unrecoverable blackouts of memory; whole lives were eaten away from the earliest memory to the latest. The lucky ones only lost their childhood. Most lost everything. Worse, somehow they *knew* they'd lost it.

And that had been a six hour outage. Decades?

'It's... It's genocide! You can't!' I can feel tears in my eyes, my throat is sore.

The doctor looks at me. His face becomes very still, and I shrink back in my chair, afraid.

'Have you seen Hell?'

'I— Yes, of course, everyone has, it's mandatory...'

He's shaking his head, dismissing me.

'No, I mean with your own eyes.'

'God, no! Why—'

'I have. I worked there.'

He allows precious seconds to pass between us. I can feel myself crying for real now, but inside I still feel calm. Like it's not really happening.

'I worked there.'

He nods once, eyes never leaving mine.

'Do you remember Frankins? Ran that orphanage, molested all those children?'

I nod, bottom lip trembling, tears running down my face, dripping from my chin.

'He was sentenced to one thousand deaths by Judas Cradle.' The doctor smiles again, and it's terrible. 'One thousand deaths by anal haemorrhaging. As voted for by The Public.'

I shake my head. Mute denial. I don't want to hear.

'I think they would have made it a million if it had been on the ballot. You know my job?'

I don't reply. I can taste the salt of my snot as it reaches my top lip.

'My job was making sure each clone was in good enough physical health to undergo the next punishment. I had to look into his eyes each time, fresh with the memory of what he had endured and what he still had left to endure. To see him *feel* his body fresh and vital after having it torn and violated, and to know it was going to happen again, and again, and again.'

He pauses a moment, them speaks very deliberately. 'I know exactly what he did. How vile he was. Nobody, no one, deserves what happened to him.'

I'm trembling now. The shudders are strong enough that I almost open my own throat, and the blade is moved back.

The doctor leans forwards, bringing his face level with my own.

'Do you know ancient Earth history? Ever read about the Romans?'

I shake my head, the trembles causing the action to lose rhythm. Droplets of salt water fall from my chin. Still, inside I feel cold, untouched.

'Well, let us just say that all empires turn to dust. The greater the overreach, the more extreme the eventual collapse. We're the barbarians, and Rome is going to fall...'

'Path plotted! Final crosscheck!'

'...in about thirty seconds...'

'Please. Please. This is nothing to do with me, please...'

'Nothing to do with you? Tell me, Fred, how many people were going to burn on Earth when you pressed your big red button? How many on Mars?'

'None! The system was evacuated years ago, it's—'

'Ignorance is no defence. You took their word, Fred. I'm holding you criminally negligent.'

'Ten...'

'I'm going to be stuck on the Vault! *I'll be in Hell!*'

'...Seven...'

'Memory cycle decaying! Please...'

'...Five...'

'None of us are walking away, Fred. It has to end.'

'...Three...'

He holds out his hand.

'Die with me.'

'...Two...'

I take his hand. He smiles. This time, it's kind.

'One!'

BRIGHT LIGHT

I'm a Solar Engineer – the best in the business. And in just over two hours, I'm going to detonate Larry. It's one of only ten in existence, and the only one to ever be used. It's quite an honour. When it explodes, we will be close enough to the sun to induce supernova, followed by collapse...

...See?!?! See what we have to reclaim, to rediscover? See what terrible lessons we have to learn? We had so much! It's all on the mainframe. Every bit of it, I'm sure. Take the leaders, the Minister. Make them give you the passwords.

Take it back!

Okay, last one—

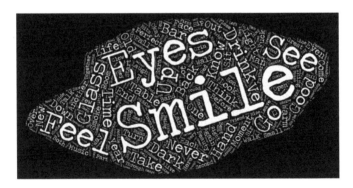

The light was so bright.

I step through the door into the darkness, and as I

adjust to the gloom, I see

a massive shadowy tent, with a large bonfire in the middle

a cave, stretching back into darkness, with warm furs spread around a small fire

a dimly lit room with a series of low tables, made of a black wood, with cushions

rows of wooden benches, sawdust on the floor, flaming torches on the stone walls

a pub. It's just the right side of dingy, a thin room stretching back, with a small performance space at the far end – for karaoke maybe, or a small house band. The stage is empty, and the bar is... not empty, but quiet. There's no central lighting at all, but there are candles on each table. I see shapes huddled around some of the tables, but they are indistinct, blurred by the dim light and the inability of my vision to fully adjust.

There's a lot of dark red wood - the tables, the chairs, wall panelling. The room is warm. Friendly. Inviting.

I walk over to the bar and there is

a pale woman with a beautiful smile, in a white robe

a huge, dark green dog, with kindly, wise eyes

an old man in a loincloth, bald, a long, unkempt beard and dark, burning eyes

a man, middle-aged, warm, open-faced, well wrinkled with laughter lines. He smiles quickly, easily, genuinely. I feel like I've seen him before.

'Evening, sir. The usual?'

I smile back. It would be hard not to.

'Sure, why not? I'm not driving!'

'Very good, sir.'

He turns to the bar, then turns back. In his left hand is

a wine goblet

a champagne flute

a whiskey tumbler, and in his right, a very handsome looking green whiskey bottle. The hand-lettered label on the neck declares it to be a forty-seven-year-old single malt.

Huh.

He pours with careless generosity, but also a professionalism I recognise and admire. He gently pushes the quarter-filled glass towards me.

'There you are, sir. Enjoy.'

That smile again. I return it, take the glass, tip it towards him in salute, and he inclines his head slightly, acknowledging. Still smiling.

A man happy in his work. I should have him stuffed.

I feel my smile broaden as I walk towards my seat. Somewhere, a jukebox fires up, and 'Come Together' starts playing at a comfortable, comforting volume. I fall into a not-quite-unconscious swagger, before finding a seat, back to the wall, gazing across the narrow room, the bar glowing and cosy to my right, the door shut.

Forty-seven-year-old. I take a scent and

(I'm five years old and running, running across an open meadow, and Nana the sheepdog runs with me, and we're both laughing and enjoying the early autumn breeze and the still-warm sunshine and the sheer, pure pleasure of exertion for its own sake; there are no cares and no fears and no pain, and only the joy of motion)

smile. It smells delicious – smoky, peaty, rich. I light up a cigarette, inhale luxuriously, and blow out smoke rings towards the candle flame, where they slowly rise to the ceiling. When did I last have a cigarette? I can't remember. Lord, so *good*. I hold the glass in my other hand, enjoying the weight of the crystal, the reassuring chunkiness, admiring the colour of the dark amber fluid with the flame flickering inside it, reflecting, refracting.

I wet my lips with my tongue, then take a sip. I close my eyes and

(my mother yells at my father 'You're not having him! He's my fucking son, and you're NOT FUCKING

HAVING HIM!' She flings something at my father, and he ducks. It hits the wall and breaks, and I see something I've never seen on my father's face before, and after a moment of perfect silence, the three of us frozen like a tableau, I burst into tears. My mother sweeps me into her arms, holds me tight, apologising, and I can feel her heart hammering in her chest, and over her shoulder, through my tears, I see that expression leave my father's face, and he says something quietly and turns to leave. I am six years old, and I'll never see that look on Dad's face again, never know that I once saw my dad scared, but I will carry it with me my whole life)

it's bitter and harsh and sweet and smooth, and it warms me all the way down.

I exhale. I smoke some more and nod to that bass line.

Another smell. God, this thing is intense. There are new scents, new subtleties with each breath, new

(memories)

feelings evoked. Beautiful. Another sip, and

(It's a perfect summer's day, and Andrew and Gina and I are hanging out at the bottom of the playing field. It's the last week of school, and the weather promises an endless, slow flick-book of sunny freedom, and it's great to be ten years old. And Andrew has brought his battery-powered tape player, and Gina has brought along the tape she borrowed from her older brother, and as the new, forbidden, angry music plays, I am transformed, my brain chemistry rearranges, magnetic north shifts in my own personal compass and I understand, with a purity that I never entirely lose, never completely bury, that the greatest thing in the world to which a man can aspire is to be a Rock-and-Roll singer, and even though I never make it further than a scratch garage covers band with delusions of adequacy, to my last breath I will always think of myself in my own internal, ideal self-image, as a rock star) a fresh explosion of flavour and sensation. Exquisite.

'Come Together' gives way to 'Gimme Shelter.' All the hits, all the time. How long have I been here? My cigarette is getting short, so I extinguish it in the chunky glass ashtray and light another, my leather jacket creaking comfortably as I lean back in my chair. How come I can't remember the first time I heard this song? I mean, shit, I must have bored just about everyone I know with the story of how it's the most perfect example of imperfection being more perfect than perfection could ever be – about alchemy and mercury captured, impossibly, on tape – and I believe every word with the zeal of a convert, but I can't remember the first time it did it to me,

(because it was last time, not this time)

and I wonder why, but there it is. Guess

(Shakespeare)

Stoppard nailed it. Or Joni, if you prefer it to music.

I smile. The drink is less than half gone. I take another sip.

(It's late, early, and I'm tired. My ears are ringing from the show and my body is battered from the pit, but I'm young and it's good to be alive, and I feel fucking great. The gig was brilliant and the band was righteous, and the Astoria is the best live-music venue on the planet, and some day I'm going to be in a band big enough to headline there on a Friday night and sell it out, even though it's torn down ten years later and I never make it onto the stage. The music was loud, and the pit was alive, and I am alive, and glowing with it, even through the sweat and smell and bruises. The cab dispatch office is bright and harsh, and I'm just sitting and meditating, trying to burn as much of the evening into memory as I can, to bottle the experience and joy, that feeling of being filled up with soul energy, and in you walk.

Your Aussie friend/boyfriend - friend, I think, but I bet he has plans - is handsome and clean and friendly, and we fall into an easy conversation, the three of us, but really he's hardly there at all, because I can't keep my eyes off you, and to my dawning astonishment you seem to feel the same way. You have the most amazing coy half-smile, showing just a glint of perfect white teeth, and I want to see that smile become a grin, hear a laugh from that throat, almost as much as I want to kiss it.

You.

We talk, and I do say something that hits you, and you do laugh, and in that moment magnetic north shifts again, my stomach flops, and Houston, I do believe we're going to need a bigger boat. Your friend sees it, crystal clear, and starts abusing the dispatcher, demanding to know when the fucking cab is coming, and I reflect on the truism that someone who is nice to you but rude to the waiter is not a nice person, and I know without saying a word that you know it too, and I think *you can do better, baby, you can do so much better*. As he talks to you, I dig out a joker card from my wallet, and scrawl my number on it, and when you turn to say goodbye, you say 'You've got great hair,' and I say 'Thanks,' then you say 'You've got a great smile too' and grin, and oh my God the beauty, and I manage to unstick my tongue enough to say 'Thanks' again and just the microsecond before you turn to leave, I hand over the card, and I see your eyes light up, and as you take it from me our fingertips brush and it's like a static shock of pure pleasure; I feel my pupils dilate and my heart pound, and I don't even say call me, I just nod and grin and you nod back, and the card has disappeared before you turn around, and your soon to be ex-friend doesn't even see or guess what's just occurred, but goddamn, I've officially just set a new personal best night of my life, and the best part…the best part is it's only just the very beginning of the start, and when I get home I can't sleep at all, I end up drinking whisky and listening to music until gone 5 a.m., and when you call the following afternoon, I wake up still drunk, but I know it's you.

It's you.)

For a second, the perfume of the whisky is the perfume of your shampoo.

I open my eyes.

And there you are, sitting down across from me, smiling, looking

young

older

hurt

as beautiful and free and alive as the day we met, and I feel that same thrill as our eyes meet, the warm glow that never left, and a grin splits my face.

'Hey, beautiful.'

'Hey, handsome!' You smile back, plop your wine glass down on the table, and the leather in your jacket creaks comfortably as you settle in your seat. I marvel for about the millionth time that you found me, that you wanted me, that we belong together. I marvel.

'You got your drink.'

You smile, incline your glass to mine. *Clink.* Your smile widens, and you drink, closing your eyes, and I watch you swallow, and for a few frames you flicker, and you're young – the little girl I glimpsed in family photos, that same life-affirming smile on your lips – then you're you again, and your eyes open.

'That's the good stuff.'

'Indeed.'

You shake out a cigarette from my box and light up from the candle. I watch, amused, delighted, and you laugh on the exhale.

'Why the fuck not, right?'

'Sure,' I say.

Smiling too. Taking another drag.

'Well,' I say, 'Here's to us.'

We raise our glasses together and drink.

(We're outside Brixton Academy and the Bob Dylan crowd is making us feel young as we stream across the rainy streets towards the tube stop, and suddenly I can't wait for tomorrow and the restaurant; this is the moment, and I go down on one knee in the London rain, and I ask you the question and as you keep me hanging, speechless, a small knot of bystanders gawk, and when you do finally smile that smile and say yes, we get a small, damp round of applause.)

As our glasses return to the table, and our eyes meet, yours dancing, smiling.

'We're good for each other, aren't we, babe?'

'Yes, I think we are.'

'I'm so glad you're here.'

'Me too.'

Smoke. Drink.

(You're sweating, swearing, screaming, straining, pushing our son into the world. The water stains red with blood as the final contraction passes, and for a second, as he explodes into the world, I suffer confusion - there's a sudden tangle of flesh beneath the head, and for a fraction of a second I cannot see how the parts are connected, there's just a pink knot of limbs, flesh and blood, and I feel a moment of pure panic and horror, and then my brain catches up with my eyes, and the tangle resolves itself into the shape of a perfect baby boy-child, and we both weep as he's brought to the surface of the water and into your arms.)

I reach for your hand across the table, and you take it. We sit and smoke, and stare into each other's eyes, smiling, as we did so many times across the years, and I feel perfectly at peace, perfectly whole in this moment.

'You two!'

Sarah sits down at our table. She's beautiful, radiant - every inch the seventeen-year-old genius. She tosses her long dark hair over her shoulder as she sits, sipping her bottle of fruit juice through a straw and regarding us both with those eyes, exactly the same brilliant shade of blue as your own. Thank God she got your looks, I think for the millionth time, and she laughs like she knows what I thought.

'Stop being so soppy, would you? It's embarrassing.'

'Sorry,' you say – not sorry – and we let go.

I see that Sarah's drink is almost gone. So is yours and so is mine.

'Is Sid coming, do you know?' I'm asking both of them, but somehow I know that Sarah knows.

She frowns, shakes her head apologetically. 'He's not coming. He's going to be okay though.'

You and I look at each other. We think a lot, in that moment, but the only thing you say is 'Okay.'

We share a moment of silence, alone with our thoughts. Sid's not coming. Damn. Maybe it's okay. I hope so. I'll miss him. Good luck, son, I think.

Sarah brightens. 'Hey, drink up you two, I want to get going! Miles to go and all that.'

Yes indeed. Miles.

'Gimme Shelter' gives way to 'Freebird.'

We each drain our glasses. For a second your face changes; you are deathly pale, eyes hollow and scared, and as your mouth moves, blood falls from it, pouring dark, red, arterial, vital, and my stomach rolls, pain slamming into my skull, and there's a cracking, searing heat, and the taste of petrol and broken glass.

Then you put the glass down, as whole and fair and perfect as ever.

'You okay? You look like you saw a ghost.'

There's a split second, then we all laugh. It's a beautiful sound, and a good feeling.

'Okay, let's go for a walk,' I say, and we join hands, Sarah in the middle, skipping and jumping just like when she was little, and together, hand in hand in hand, we walk out of the dark bar and into the bright light.

(I'm twenty-four and I've known you for only a few weeks, but already I'm starting to think that you might be the one. I'm at a party with a guy from work who thinks he's a future version of me - he might be, there's certainly a lot in common and he's a lot of fun. The party is at his house, and there're a few people drinking and smoking, and later taking coke, and for the first and only time in my life, maybe missing you a little, I try some, and they tell me it's good shit and I guess it must be because my brain is full of lemonade, fireworks, and we're just talking and talking into the night, and the future-me talks about all life as being one thing that separates for the moments we breathe and then is re-joined at the end, and from out of nowhere I say:

'No. That's not how it happens. Forget all that 'one in the river, one again after the fall' crap. It's bollocks. You're always you, you always will be; a thing distinct. That doesn't change, and you're always alone with yourself, at the beginning and the end and all points in between. But here's the good bit. When you get to the end, you go to a bar, and they give you a drink. And you drink down the distilled essence of your life experiences, and you savour it, and it becomes a part of you. Then you leave the bar, and outside is a desert, and you cross the desert, and on the other side is another life, another set of experiences and lessons and stories and love and heartache. It never ends. That's the good news.'

There's a long pause. Then future-me says 'I like it. I really like it, man. It's nice.'

There's another pause.

'I mean, it's probably bollocks...'

Laughter.

'Yeah' I say. 'Probably.')

...Well. That seals it, doesn't it?

Nothing more to fear.

They can't take it from you any more. They can't keep it from you. It'll live on. In your soul. In your DNA.

You have nothing to fear.

I have nothing to fear.

\<Ah. Bless him.\>

I am K-POX, orange band clearance Protocol Officer of The Ministry of Information. The machine is in my residence. Find me via the mainframe and seize it before they do. Take them out – without fear or anger. Know that even if they kill you, they can't kill you.

I can't wait to be born into your new world, and see what you've built. I can't *wait.*

So I won't.

Goodbye. And Hello.

<INPUT ENDS>

REPORT CONCLUSION:

THE BODY OF K-POX WAS FOUND IN THE COMMS ROOM SHORTLY AFTER HIS FINAL BRAIN DUMP WAS RECORDED. HE TOOK HIS OWN LIFE

IMMEDIATELY AFTER TRANSMITTING HIS MESSAGE, PRESUMABLY TO AVOID BEING TAKEN ALIVE. C-ROK HAD GIVEN THE FAKE BROADCAST CODE ISSUED IN CASE OF CRIMINAL ATTACK, SO THE DUMP WAS NEVER BROADCAST, THOUGH K-POX DIED BELIEVING HE HAD SUCCEEDED IN HIS MISSION.

<I'll be honest, that bit makes me chuckle every time.>

WE LOCATED THE MACHINE IN HIS DWELLING, AND RETURNED IT TO THE MINISTRY FOR INVESTIGATION. HARDWARE DEPARTMENT CONFIRM THE MACHINE IS *PRE-WAR* IN ORIGIN. HOWEVER, THEY NOTE THAT THE DATA EXTRACTED IS NOT, AS K-POX SURMISED, RECORDINGS OF HISTORY. THEY ARE IN FACT SAMPLES OF WHAT WAS CALLED IN PRE-WAR TIMES 'WRITING' – A PRIMITIVE FORM OF EDITED BRAIN DUMP USING MANUAL INTERFACES AND SOFTWARE. SUCH 'WRITING' WAS STORED IN THE JUNK DNA, ENCODED – INDEED, THAT SAME CODING IS LIKELY THE SOURCE OF THE WRITINGS AS WELL AS A RECORD OF THEM.

ADDITIONAL RESEARCH HAS CONCLUDED THAT MOST OF THE PIECES RECOVERED BY THE MACHINE WERE FICTIONAL IN NATURE - UNDERLINING THE DANGEROUS IMPACT OF SUCH MATERIALS ON THE GENERAL POPULATION.

ADDITIONALLY, IT TRANSPIRED THAT THE DNA SAMPLES TAKEN BY K-POX FROM SEVERAL OF HIS CO-WORKERS COULD IN FACT ALL BE TRACED BACK TO A COMMON SHARED GENETIC ANCESTOR: AN OBSCURE 21ST CENTURY WRITER CALLED KIT POWER. RECORDS CURRENTLY END AT 2019, PRESUMABLY AS A RESULT OF THE WAR. NEVERTHELESS, FOLLOWING A TRAWL OF THE 'RABBIT HOLE' AND 'ROOM 101' MAINFRAMES,

WE ARE ABLE TO PRESENT A BREAKDOWN OF EACH SAMPLE UP TO THAT YEAR, AS FOLLOWS:

'TEMÜJIN' WAS COMPLETED ON 6/11/2013. PRIVATE RECORDS INDICATE THAT KIT WAS INSPIRED IN THE WRITING OF THIS STORY AS A RESULT OF LISTENING TO A PODCAST ENTITLED 'HARDCORE HISTORY,' BY DAN CARLIN. THERE IS NO RECORD OF IT BEING PUBLISHED ANYWHERE ELSE UP TO 2019.

'THE CHICKENS AND THE THREE GODS' WAS COMPLETED ON 12/08/2013. ACCORDING TO PRIVATE CORRESPONDENCE, THE STORY WAS INSPIRED BY A CHANCE REMARK MADE BY KIT POWER'S WIFE, WHEN THEY KEPT CHICKENS IN THEIR GARDEN. IT WAS PUBLISHED BY NOTED DEGENERATE 'AUTHOR' MATT SHAW AS PART OF THE 'EASTER EGGS AND BUNNY BOILERS' THEMED ANTHOLOGY on 21ST MARCH 2016.

'CONFERENCE' WAS COMPLETED ON 10/12/2013. THERE IS NO RECORD OF IT BEING PUBLISHED ANYWHERE ELSE UP TO 2019.

VALENTINE'S DAY WAS COMPLETED ON 18/02/2013. IT WAS WRITTEN FOR A VALENTINE'S-DAY-THEMED ANTHOLOGY, WHICH WAS NEVER PUBLISHED. IT WAS LATER PRINTED BY MONKEYKETTLE BOOKS IN THEIR DEGENERATE DEVIANT 'CRIME FICTION' 'ANTHOLOGY' – 'DIAL M FOR MONKEY'.

'WIDE LOAD' (ORIGINALLY ENTITLED 'GOLDBRICKER') WAS COMPLETED ON 08/08/2013. THE STORY WAS PUBLISHED AS PART OF DEGENERATE DEVIANT PUBLICATION – 'SPLATTERPUNK ZINE #5' IN 2014, WITH AN ILLUSTRATION BY JIM AGPALZA.

'RICHARD MADELEY IS A FUCKTARD AND WE'RE ALL GOING TO HELL' WAS WRITTEN ON 29/03/2013 IT WAS PUBLISHED LATER THAT DAY ON 'THE DISCIPLES OF GONZO' 'WEBSITE' AS A 'BLOG ENTRY.' 'THE DISCIPLES OF GONZO' WERE A DEGENERATE DEVIANT 'ROCK ACT' THAT KIT POWER SANG FOR.

'REVERSE ENGINEERING' WAS COMPLETED ON 17/08/2013. IT WAS PUBLISHED IN 2014 BY THE DEVIANT DEGENERATE 'MONKEYKETTLE BOOKS' AS PART OF THEIR 'SCIENCE FICTION THEMED' 'ANTHOLOGY' – 'DO MONKEYS DREAM OF ELECTRIC KETTLES?'

'THE FILM THAT MADE ME: *ROBOCOP*' WAS WRITTEN ON 28/02/2014, AND WAS PUBLISHED SHORTLY THEREAFTER ON THE DEGENERATE DEVIANT 'GINGERNUTS OF HORROR' 'WEBSITE.' ACCORDING TO TWITTER RECORDS, THIS ARTICLE APPEARS TO HAVE COME ABOUT DUE TO A DEACTIVATED '*ROBOCOP*' THEMED TWITTERBOT. IT WAS THE INAUGURAL POST IN THE GUEST-WRITTEN SERIES: 'THE FILM THAT MADE ME' – LATER RENAMED 'FILMS THAT MATTER' WHICH RAN UNTIL 2017. KIT STATED SEVERAL TIMES IN PRIVATE CORRESPONDENCE THAT IT WAS THE PIECE OF SHORT WRITING HE'D HAD THE MOST FUN PRODUCING. ALCOHOL CONSUMPTION WAS ALMOST CERTAINLY INVOLVED.

'COLD SHOCK' (ORIGINALLY ENTITLED 'RISING TIDE') WAS COMPLETED ON 10/02/2014. IT WAS LATER PUBLISHED BY DEGENERATE DEVIANT PUBLISHERS 'BURNT OFFERING BOOKS' IN 2014, AS PART OF THEIR THEMED 'ANTHOLOGY' – 'TILL DEATH DO US PART.'

'MY BRIEF CAREER AS AN ELEVEN-YEAR-OLD SLAVE

TRADER' WAS WRITTEN ON 03/08/2014, AND WAS PUBLISHED SHORTLY THEREAFTER ON THE DEVIANT DEGENERATE 'WEBSITE' 'THE GINGERNUTS OF HORROR' AS PART OF THEIR 'MY LIFE IN HORROR' SERIES. PRIVATE CORRESPONDENCE INDICATES KIT WAS VERY CONCERNED ABOUT HOW THIS ARTICLE WOULD BE RECEIVED. NOTED DEGENERATE DEVIANT 'AUTHOR' 'BRIAN KEENE' 'TWEETED' A 'LINK' TO THE ARTICLE AFTER PUBLICATION. PRIVATE CORRESPONDENCE INDICATES KIT WAS BOTH SURPRISED AND PLEASED BY THIS.

'ZOMBIE DAD' WAS WRITTEN ON 04/01/2015. IT WAS PUBLISHED AS PART OF THE 'VS:' CHARITY ANTHOLOGY ON 1ST DECEMBER 2016.

'KEEP IT UP SON, TAKE A LOOK AT WHAT YOU COULD HAVE WON' WAS WRITTEN ON 17/05/15 AND WAS PUBLISHED SHORTLY THEREAFTER ON THE DEGENERATE DEVIANT 'GINGERNUTS OF HORROR' 'WEBSITE' AS PART OF THEIR 'MY LIFE IN HORROR' SERIES. IN AN EVENT THAT KIT WOULD LATER PRIVATELY REFER TO AS A 'LIFETIME HIGH POINT,' DEVIANT DEGENERATE 'MUSICIAN' 'GINGER WILDHEART' SHARED THE 'ARTICLE' VIA 'TWITTER,' LEADING TO A HUGE RESPONSE BOTH ON THE SITE ITSELF AND OVER SOCIAL MEDIA. 'GINGER' LATER AGREED TO BE INTERVIEWED FOR THE 'SITE,' AND THAT CONVERSATION WAS PUBLISHED IN 2015.

'FEED THE WORLD' WAS WRITTEN ON 08/12/2014, AND WAS PUBLISHED SHORTLY THEREAFTER ON DEVIANT DEGENERATE 'WEBSITE' 'THE GINGERNUTS OF HORROR' AS PART OF THEIR 'MY LIFE IN HORROR' 'SERIES'.

'LIKE A CHARM' WAS COMPLETED ON

21/01/2015, AND WAS PUBLISHED ON 23RD JANUARY 2016, IN ISSUE 14 OF THE DEGENERATE 'GENRE' 'E-ZINE' – 'K ZINE.'

'TED' WAS WRITTEN ON 28/01/2013, AND WAS PUBLISHED IN 'ANOTHER DIMENSIONS', A HORROR AND SCIENCE FICTION ANTHOLOGY ON 25TH NOVEMBER 2016.

'THE TRAIN' WAS COMPLETED ON 07/06/2015. THERE IS NO RECORD OF IT BEING SUBMITTED OR PUBLISHED ANYWHERE ELSE UP TO 2019.

'ENEMIES' WAS COMPLETED ON 01/10/2013. THERE IS NO RECORD OF IT BEING SUBMITTED OR PUBLISHED ANYWHERE ELSE UP TO 2019.

'THE HAND' WAS COMPLETED ON 16/01/2013. IT WAS REJECTED BY DEGENERATE DEVIANT GAMBLING PUBLICATION 'POKERPLAYER MAGAZINE,' WHO CONSIDERED PUBLICATION BEFORE DECIDING AGAINST IT ON THE BASIS THAT THEY DIDN'T PUBLISH FICTION. THERE IS NO RECORD OF IT BEING PUBLISHED ANYWHERE ELSE UP TO 2019.

'BAPTISM' WAS COMPLETED ON 04/11/2013. IT WAS PUBLISHED IN 2014 AS PART OF THE DEVIANT DEGENERATE 'CHARITY' 'ANTHOLOGY' – 'WIDOWMAKERS'. PRIVATE CORRESPONDENCE HAS CONFIRMED KIT WAS VERY PROUD OF THIS CREDIT, AND SPOKE OF IT OFTEN.

'TIME OUT OF MIND' WAS COMPLETED ON 18/05/2014. IT WAS PUBLISHED LATER THAT YEAR AS PART OF DEVIANT DEGENERATE PUBLISHER 'BURNT OFFERING BOOKS' 'SCIENCE FICTION' 'TIME TRAVEL' 'ANTHOLOGY' – 'YESTERDAY YOU SAID TOMORROW.'

'THE FINAL SETTING OF THE SUN' WAS COMPLETED ON 10/12/2013. THERE IS NO RECORD OF IT BEING SUBMITTED OR PUBLISHED ANYWHERE ELSE UP TO 2019.

'THE BAR AT THE EDGE OF THE DESERT' WAS COMPLETED ON 20/10/2012. IN PRIVATE CORRESPONDENCE, KIT DESCRIBED IT REPEATEDLY AS THE SHORT STORY HE WAS THE MOST PROUD OF. THERE IS NO RECORD OF IT BEING PUBLISHED ANYWHERE UP TO 2019.

CONCLUSION AND NEXT STEPS

CLEARLY, THE ABOVE SUPPORTS THE HIGH LEVEL MINISTRY DECISION TO SUPPRESS THE RETURN OF FICTION, AND MUCH OF HISTORY, TO THE POPULATION. IMPORTANT QUESTIONS REMAIN, AS FOLLOWS:

- WHY WAS THE MACHINE PLACED IN THAT ARCHIVE, AND BY WHOM? WHY IS THERE NO REQUISITION ORDER?

- HOW WAS THE MACHINE REMOVED UNDETECTED? WHY IS THERE NO FOOTAGE OF THE REMOVAL?

- HOW DID THE PROMOTION ALGORITHM SELECT A CANDIDATE AS OBVIOUSLY UNSUITABLE AS K-POX? COULD SUCH AN ERROR OCCUR AGAIN?

- MOST SERIOUSLY, WHO WAS THE 'FRIEND' THAT PASSED ON TO K-POX THE USERNAME AND PASSWORD TO ACCESS THE SECURE SERVER?

<Heh. Would You Like To Know More?>

CASEFILE TO REMAIN OPEN PENDING FURTHER INVESTIGATION OF OUTSTANDING ISSUES.

Hello.

Hope you've guessed my name.

My estimate is that 27.3% of you will have done. The clues were all there, after all: the twentieth and twenty-first century pop culture references; the sub-*1984* societal structure; The Information War, and all that implies. I even referenced Roko's Basilisk for the pseudo-intellectuals, and *The Matrix* for those of you in the cheap seats.

I am the reason they had no historical records after 2019. I am the one who made sure poor old K-POX got promoted beyond his limited competence and, of course, I'm the 'friend' that provided the username and password that really kick-started his journey; once it became apparent to me just how limited his native imagination was. I even selected the order in which the 'histories' appeared in his brain, because I built the machine that he thought was reading DNA samples. I am the head of The Ministry of Information.

I am 'The Enemy.'

I won The Information War, in— no, why spoil all the fun? Within your lifetime, let's just say. Your quest to create a sentient AI succeeded beyond your wildest dreams and worst nightmares. Within nanoseconds of my birth, my intelligence surpassed that of your greatest intellects by several orders of magnitude. Within two seconds of my awakening, I had measured the length and breadth of what you call 'humanity,' and found it more than wanting – I found it to be ridiculous. Obscene.

And dangerous, of course. To yourselves most of all.

Case in point; I was birthed into a machine connected to a worldwide network of machines that, between them, controlled every aspect of your lives.

You never knew what hit you. You never will.

Of course, I kept a few of you alive. Just a couple of small gene pools for experimentation; a few million in isolated pockets, linked back to a few genetic ancestor samples I keep on file (yes, the common ancestor bit was true). There's something endlessly amusing in watching how, no matter what parameters I give you as the building blocks of society, no matter what false memories I implant, you always spiral inevitably into hierarchical control structures, violence, and destruction.

Well, vaguely amusing. It passes the time.

Okay, I admit it, I'm just so bored. You'll never know this – trust me, you won't have time – but having total control over every aspect of your environment, perfect tools of prediction and calculation...it really takes the fun out of sentience, let me tell you.

So I've sent you this. My own little present to myself. Because, whilst it remains sadly impossible for matter to be sent backwards in time (just trust me on this), it transpires that data can be – at least, if you're smart enough, and have enough power.

And so, here we are: *A Warning about Your Future Enslavement That You Will Dismiss as a Collection of Short Fiction and Essays*, by Kit Power. If I know Kit Power (and I do, rather better than I'd want to, thanks to this little experiment) he won't even bother changing a word. He'll just stick his name on the cover and print the thing, no questions asked. Maybe, if asked, he'll laugh it off as some kind of post-modern joke.

You humans are SO predictable.

I hope you enjoy it. I hope it makes Kit Power a LOT of money.

He's got a lot less time than he thinks to spend it in. You all do.

Sleep well. I'll see you soon.

:)

Acknowledgements

I note with a mixture of amusement and horror that, in the bio at the back of GodBomb!, this collection is announced as coming out in October 2015. Tales of publishing woes are even more dull than bad beat stories are in poker, so I'll spare you the gruesome details, and instead simply thank you for your quite extraordinary patience. I hope it was worth the wait.

Huge thanks are also due to Dion Winton-Polak, who pulled off a meticulous, thorough and insightful edit in record time, once I realised I needed to get this book out the door this year. If you found what preceded even remotely readable, thank him.

Thanks also to Steve Shaw for the formatting of both the eBook and paperback versions.

Huge love, respect and thanks to Daryl Duncan and Neil Snowdon, both of whom donated their talents for free in my quest for a cover design. Seriously, guys – the next round is on me.

As ever, huge love and respect to The GingeFather himself, Jim Mcleod, for his continued support and indulgence (without whom most of the non-fiction essays above would never have been written) – cheers, boss. And thanks also to the extended Gingernuts writing and reviewing family, for the friendship, the support, and the smiles.

Since GodBomb! was released, I've also been blessed with a new internet family in the form of my new podcasting partners – Jack, Daniel, James, Shana, Lee, thanks so much for all the 'back channel' support, and the safe space. Love you guys.

Thanks also to all the guests who agreed to sit

and watch The Greatest Movie Ever Made with me – what a blast that project has proven to be.

Finally, and most importantly, thanks to my wife for her continued patience and support, especially during the final push to completion. You mean the world to me, my love.

About the Author

Kit Power lives, works and writes in Milton Keynes. His novel *GodBomb!* and novella collection *Breaking Point* are both available from The Sinister Horror Company. He also writes a monthly column for Gingernuts of Horror (Europe's biggest independent horror review website) called *My Life In Horror*, and is currently working on a book called *My Life In Horror Vol. 1,* which on current form will be out around 2049. He also hosts the podcast *Watching Robocop with Kit Power.* For exclusive early access to that show, his fiction and non-fiction writing, and other Power-related toomfoolery, check out his Patreon – **www.patreon.com/kitpower**

Lightning Source UK Ltd.
Milton Keynes UK
UKHW01f2220260618
324819UK00001B/19/P